Advanced Connections™

Participant Book

Michael Hovland

Ludie Dickeson

Karen Holtkamp

ISBN 1-887842-05-5 (Participant Book)
ISBN 1-887842-04-7 (Complete program)

Noel-Levitz
2350 Oakdale Boulevard
Coralville, Iowa 52241-9702 USA

Contents

Advanced Connections

Facilitator/group leader _____

Phone _____

Other participants   Phone

_____   _____

_____   _____

_____   _____

_____   _____

_____   _____

_____   _____

_____   _____

_____   _____

_____   _____

_____   _____

_____   _____

_____   _____

_____   _____

_____   _____

_____   _____

_____   _____

_____   _____

_____   _____

SESSION ONE: Building a Service Culture _____

SECTION 1: Introduction

Welcome to Advanced Connections™! This program focuses on advanced service skills, teamwork, problem prevention and many other topics that will help you and your campus move to a higher level of service excellence.

By developing your service skills you can ensure the best service to the people you help and the best relationships with the people you work with. But service excellence requires more than individual excellence. It also requires that individuals and offices work together to build a service culture on campus.

Throughout Advanced Connections you'll learn about and have time to practice a variety of advanced service skills. You'll also spend time looking at your role in helping the campus build a service culture—a culture essential to your institution's efforts to improve student/customer satisfaction.

The most important benefit from this program, though, is how it will make you feel. Helping others makes you feel good. By giving you the tools to develop your skills, Advanced Connections can help you feel even better about your service.

Key Concepts of Advanced Connections
• Quality service demands good individual skills *and* the support of customer-centered systems, policies and procedures.
• Everyone has a role in meeting campus-wide service goals.
• Advanced Connections is about practicing and improving individual service skills, building teamwork, improving systems and preventing problems.
• To consistently provide quality service, staff, faculty and administrators have to work together to build a service culture.

What Is a Service Culture?

Like any culture, a service culture has its own philosophy, shared by each of its members, who hold expectations of behaving toward each other in certain ways. In a service culture, members share the philosophy that serving both external and internal customers is of prime importance. A campus with a service culture strives for outstanding service and uses that outstanding service as a method for achieving success.

Every college and university has areas of service excellence—individuals and offices that provide high quality service and who work continually to improve that service. The goal of Advanced Connections is to build on these existing strengths so that more and more internal and external customers on your campus will be touched by service excellence.

Session One Topics

Recognizing quality service. What makes up quality service? More importantly, how can you recognize quality service in your own work? Quality service is more than a smile or making eye contact. Delivering quality service demands that you continually evaluate what the people around you need and find out how you can best fulfill those needs.

Often people don't know what they need, or if they know, they may be unsure how to ask for it. Being able to recognize the needs of others and help them get the information they want is only a small part of quality service. Going beyond the expectations to predict what the future needs of a customer might be is the key to outstanding customer service. By learning to recognize quality service, you can begin to develop your own skills of looking beyond the current basic needs of each customer and anticipating their future needs as well.

Assessing your own service delivery.
Before any improvement can be made, you must first discover how you are delivering quality service right now. Do you or the people in your office consistently go beyond the call of duty? Are external customers often routed to another department to get what they need? Are customers a welcome part of your day or an interruption of it? Do you value the time you spend helping a co-worker or a customer with a problem?

These and other questions are an important part of assessing the quality of service delivered in your area. It's easy to see that delivering quality service involves much more than good manners and polite telephone personalities. It demands a strong service orientation backed by comprehensive knowledge and practiced skills.

Building a service culture. After assessing the service delivery in your own area, you can begin to determine what steps to take to build a service culture throughout your institution. Building a service culture may sound like a monumental task, but really it's all about building positive relationships. Improving your

Key Indicators of a Service Culture

Here are some of the things you'll see at a college or university that has a service culture:

- People take responsibility.

- There are few barriers to communication and action.

- People are responsive to the needs of internal and external customers.

- People are friendly and courteous toward each other.

- Front-line staff frequently ask if they can be of service.

- People smile and look like they enjoy their work.

- People continuously look for ways to improve.

- Staff feel empowered to act.

Other Key Indicators of a Service Culture

- People receive positive feedback from colleagues.

- Customers are pleased after their interactions with staff.

- Administrators help staff work to improve service.

- Everyone works to identify and prevent problems.

- People work to develop customer-oriented systems, policies and procedures.

- Staff anticipate the needs of their internal and external customers.

skills at serving internal customers will strengthen your relationships with the people you work with. Improving your skills at serving external customers will help build positive relationships with the people who come to you for help.

Developing a service team. Teamwork is the backbone of any service culture. A team philosophy is crucial to providing quality service. Believing that you are an important part of a large team helps develop the impulse to respond to anyone in need in a responsible and attentive manner. Drawing on team resources and expertise lets you handle even the most difficult situations with ease and assurance.

Becoming a good team player. A team is only as good as its members. It's important to remember, however, that a team player is not the same as a follower. Teams are made up of leaders helping each other succeed. Your role as a member of a service team is an exceptional one. Your participation on the team allows you a lot of responsibility and enables you to provide the most comprehensive service possible.

Exercise 1: Building a Service Culture

Question 1) In the last vignette, why was the student upset?

Question 2) Did the staff person say or do anything wrong to the student?

Question 3) Is this problem with stereotyping the student likely to happen again with other students? Why?

Question 4) In the scene with the student, what role does the staff member have in helping to make sure this problem doesn't happen again?

Question 5) What else needs to happen to prevent problems like this from recurring?

Question 6) How can you tell if an institution has a service culture? What kinds of things would you see? What kinds of things would you hear?

Question 7) Can you identify three or four offices on your campus that have an evident service culture—offices that represent the best of your institution?

Question 8) What makes these offices stand out as the best?

SECTION 2: The Campus Run-Around

It goes by many names—red-tape, the campus-shuffle, the campus run-around. But the effect is always the same: students and other customers do a lot of unnecessary shuffling from office to office either on the phone or in person. Reducing the run-around is essential to building a service culture on campus.

You have probably encountered the run-around at some point in your experience as a customer, so you know how frustrating it can be. Take the example of moving. You might expect to fill out a change of address form for each business that you deal with: your credit card company, bank, school, etc. What gets frustrating is when you have to fill out several change of address forms for the same company!

For instance, you may discover that changing the address on your checks does not automatically change the address on your bank account. You end up filling out multiple forms and running all over the bank when a simple phone call to the account manager from the person who took your check change would have remedied the situation. When you run into just one part of a system that is not working well, the experience can turn you off to the institution as a whole. That's why it is so important to end the campus run-around for your external and internal customers. Chances are great that when your students are frustrated by the run-around, your faculty, staff and administrators will be frustrated by it as well.

The campus run-around happens for many reasons. Most campuses did not develop or expand with service in mind.

Costs of Poor Service and Poor Systems

- Lower student satisfaction
- Lower staff morale and productivity
- Inefficiency
- Waste of money and human resources

Over the years, offices are located where space is available or are located in ways that reflected reporting relationships rather than service relationships. The result often is a campus with the admissions office in one building, the registrar's office and business office in another building three blocks away, the orientation office in the student union, the advising center across the river, and faculty offices spread all over campus.

So quite literally, the run-around often means that students actually do run around from office to office all over campus to transact simple business. Worse yet, they may stand in line at each location and sometimes are told when they reach the head of the line that they should have gone to another office first. Worst of all, students may have to repeat the process at the beginning of every term or even more frequently.

Another kind of run-around can occur on the phone, when callers are transferred from office to office because staff lack information or training. When you don't have the information you need to help customers, it causes confusion, and inevitably, a run-around.

Through Advanced Connections, you can look at the way you are serving others, find ways to communicate more efficiently, increase the quality of your service and help put an end to the run-around.

Good Intentions Vs. Outstanding Service

When looking at the run-around, it is important to remember that good intentions are never enough. The person caught in a run-around has most likely received adequate service with the best intentions at each office. In the example of the bank cited earlier, the person who took your check order was most likely friendly and helpful, but didn't think ahead and consider what the change of address might mean in the overall bank system. It's the same in a campus run-around. What the customer hasn't gotten is outstanding service. What they haven't had is someone who says, "I'll take care of it." That's where you come in.

By drawing on your service-team resources, you can go beyond just adequate service and move to deliver outstanding service to students and other customers. For instance, a person might ask you a question for which you don't know the answer, although you know someone in another office who would know the answer. Instead of sending the person off, why not call that other office yourself? You will not only improve relations with the person you've helped, but with the team member you called because you won't be sending them a run-around customer.

> **Primary Causes of the Run-Around**
>
> - Staff lack knowledge of campus systems, policies and procedures.
>
> - Staff are too busy to help.
>
> - Staff don't take responsibility for customer problems.
>
> - Staff have poor access to information from other offices.
>
> - Institution has fragmented processes without concern for how students and other customers use them.
>
> - Staff are not empowered to seek solutions.

You can even go a step further and work with your team member in the other department to develop ways for you to have the information that was needed in case this same situation presents itself in the future.

The campus run-around will probably always exist to some extent, but you can significantly reduce the impact of the run-around by maintaining your commitment to building a quality service culture and relying on the support of team members to give customers the help they need instead of an exercise in frustration.

Points to Remember

- The run-around undermines student recruitment messages that highlight the campus as being convenient, user-friendly and student-centered.

- The run-around promotes a negative image of staff and their willingness to help.

- Whether customers experience the run-around in person or on the phone, it wastes time and money for many individuals and offices.

- Customers gain an impression of your institution based on their experiences with the people and the systems they find there.

- The run-around makes a campus look disorganized, bureaucratic and impersonal.

- Customers who experience the run-around are likely to become irritated or angry and may become more difficult to work with and to satisfy.

Exercise 2: Understanding the Campus Run-Around

Question 1) Have you ever seen the campus run-around in action? What do you think causes a situation like this?

Question 2) In the last vignette, how does the student likely feel and what impression does he likely have about the institution?

Question 3) Do you think the staff members and the history department chair felt they did a good job of serving the transfer student?

Question 4) What does the transfer student need? What's missing in the school's ability to help?

Question 5) How does the student run-around negatively affect staff and faculty?

11

SECTION 3: Building a Service Culture

In order to build a service culture on your campus, two things need to work hand-in-hand: the system and the staff. A customer-oriented system is the foundation of a service culture. Providing systems that give your internal and external customers the information and services they need strengthens your whole institution.

Think about examples of customer-oriented systems that you use. Perhaps it's a civic or religious organization that not only mails you a newsletter, but calls to remind you of meetings and sends you the minutes of meetings you couldn't attend. The systems that you appreciate most go the extra mile to keep you satisfied. But how can you build a customer-oriented system or make sure that your current systems are benefiting the customer?

You can begin by developing good individual service skills. As you learn to be more attentive to your customer's needs, specific areas of your system may reveal themselves as difficult for customers and will need to be changed. By using your internal service skills with the people and departments you work with, you can evaluate your system, brainstorm for ideas and find solutions to the difficulties experienced by students and staff.

Quality Systems and Quality Individual Skills Support Each Other

Customer-oriented systems help build customer-oriented skills and vice versa. Good systems make staff members want to do a better job and help you bring out the best in your institution. The better your quality service skills, the better you understand campus systems. This helps you to correct difficulties quickly and efficiently. By catching difficulties before they become problems, you can make the systems better and easier to use.

For instance, a parent calls you requesting information about "Recreation Education," a program that her child is enrolled in. You have good knowledge of your school, and you think the program may have a slightly different name, "Outdoor Recreation." You quickly call over to the department in question and learn that there is indeed a new program called "Recreation Education." There are several additional requirements that students must fulfill for this new program, and you share them with the parent on the phone.

Not only have you delivered helpful service to the parent, you have learned new information about your environment and increased your resources. That's how quality service systems and skills build on each other to help people and institutions.

Putting a Halt to the Campus Run-Around

Once you have built a solid foundation by using quality service skills to develop a customer-oriented system, you can put an end to the frustrating process of shuffling information and customers from one department to another. By using your quality service skills, you can recognize when a shuffle is taking place. By using your internal quality service skills you can take the responsibility to make improvements to your system and work with co-workers to increase your efficiency.

Let's say the parent in the previous situation had been connected to two different departments before reaching you. She had received conflicting information and was becoming angry. Your attention to quality service would enable you to recognize that there was a breakdown in communication somewhere in your system. You could use your internal quality skills to make some calls and discover the slight discrepancy between these two very similar programs. After the parent had received the current information, you could meet with the department in question and discuss ways to keep this situation from recurring.

Building a service culture takes constant effort from everyone. Working together not only improves your institution and internal workings, but makes a positive impact on the students, parents, staff and other external customers you serve. Making a significant impact on others and helping them get what they need makes everyone's job more productive and enjoyable. Enjoying each other and your job is what being part of a service culture is all about.

> ### Service Excellence: An Institutional Commitment
>
> Quality customer service, like effective student retention, does not just "happen" on an institutionwide basis. Both are products of carefully planned and integrated systems and strategies that cross the lines of traditional academic and administrative units.
>
> In both cases, the goal is to take the best of what is already happening on campus and to extend that throughout the institution.

Points to Remember

- Staff, administrators and faculty are all affected by the run-around.

- Staff, administrators and faculty all have a role in reducing the run-around.

- Reducing the run-around requires teamwork and communication.

- Reducing the run-around saves time and money.

- Your primary role is not the completion of tasks, but the delivery of quality service to customers.

- Each staff member is personally responsible for the quality of service his or her customer experiences.

Exercise 3: Putting a Halt to the Campus Run-Around

Question 1) In the last vignette, what did the secretary in the registrar's office do well?

Question 2) The secretary did a number of things well. However, what finally helped the student most?

Question 3) Which was more important to the student, the secretary's good attitude and good personal service skills or the fact that she could provide the information the student needed?

Question 4) How do good individual service skills and good systems work together to support each other?

Question 5) From the list below identify the specific approaches that would be useful in reducing or eliminating the run-around that affected the transfer student in the last vignette.

- Better communication and coordination *within* offices
- Better communication and coordination *among* offices
- Better technology
- Better orientation and training for new employees
- Better oversight of processes and systems
- More knowledge of what happens in other offices
- Training about other departments' processes and procedures

- Better orientation and information for students, so they know which departments handle what
- Monthly recognition for creative problem-solvers
- Personal commitment by all faculty, staff and administrators to reduce the run-around

Question 6) For the items you identified in Question #5, write down and discuss what ideas you have for making these approaches work (as in the following example):

Approach: Personal commitment by all to reduce the run-around

Ideas: Staff take responsibility to phone other departments for information, rather than sending the customer to that department

Approach 1: _____

Ideas: _____

_____

_____

Approach 2: _____

Ideas: _____

_____

_____

Approach 3: _____

Ideas: _____

_____

_____

Optional Activity: Meeting Recruiting Promises

Question 1) What does your institution's recruitment literature say about how students will be treated by staff and faculty at your institution?

Question 2) What does your institution's recruitment literature say about institutional convenience and ease of use?

Question 3) How does your institution actually compare to the image of the institution presented in the recruitment literature?

Question 4) What could individuals and offices do to change the institution to make it match the image of the institution presented in the recruitment literature?

SECTION 4: Your Role in Building a Service Culture

Up until now you've talked only about the *importance* of building a service culture. But how, exactly, can you help build one? In this section you will focus on the basic principles of your role in building a service culture and how you can apply these principles to your daily activities.

Keeping the Customer in Mind

A person involved in building a service culture is always thinking about the customer. Whether making decisions, solving problems or simply answering the phone, it's important for you to think about how your actions will impact the customers you deal with.

Can you recognize customer-focused behavior when you see it?

1. "We're all out of three-subject notebooks. You'll have to look somewhere else."

2. "Is there anything else I can help you with today?"

3. "Huh? Oh...I don't know."

4. "Here, let me show you how this works..."

5. "Hey, don't complain to me about it. I don't make the rules, you know!"

You could probably tell without much trouble that examples #2 and #4 showed a strong customer focus, while examples #1, #3 and #5 showed something far less than that.

What do these examples have in common? Both positive examples show a willingness to go the extra mile to help the customer. The examples of sub-par behavior stop

short. Here the service provider—loosely speaking—refuses to take responsibility for personally helping the customer.

This is not quality service at all! Quality service means doing everything you can—and then some—to make sure the customer gets what she needs. Sometimes this can mean:

- Speaking in a friendly manner when you don't feel like it
- Making phone calls to other offices to figure out how to help the customer
- Stretching the limits of your job description for the sake of the customer

A custodial person who's focused only on his job will respond to a new student's question about weekend library hours with, "Beats me, I just work here during the week!"

On the other hand, a custodial person who's focused on quality service will say instead, "I'm not sure, since I'm only here during the week. But I know where there's a campus phone directory right down the hall. You can call over to the library and find out."

See the difference? You'd better believe students and other customers can!

Building a service culture is something *every* service provider needs to do, not something you can wait around for someone else to take care of. And, of course, knowing yourself is always a good place to start. When you honestly evaluate your own attitudes and skills, you become more aware of the contributions you can make to the team and the customer service areas in which you can improve.

Anticipating Needs

Understanding what customers don't know and anticipating their needs is key to building a service culture. When you anticipate needs, you accomplish two important service goals at the same time. First, you provide better service. Second, and equally important, you help reduce problems and mistakes in the future. Remember, preventing problems is much better than dealing with problems after they happen.

By keeping the customers in mind, you are able to respond more quickly to their requests and more accurately predict their needs in order to improve your service.

> **Five Ways to Anticipate Customer Needs**
>
> Understanding what customers don't know and anticipating their needs is key to building a service culture.
>
> - Talk to students and other customers.
>
> - Use your experience to anticipate questions and anticipate needs.
>
> - Use surveys or other instruments.
>
> - Identify and monitor chronic mistakes.
>
> - Talk to your colleagues.

Getting Involved

Another important aspect of building a service culture is to keep yourself actively involved. "Passing-the-buck" behavior that leads to the campus run-around is eliminated when you take an active part in providing quality service. In a service culture, each person has the power to take responsibility for a situation and provide quality service to his or her customers. Sometimes this means recognizing problems and talking them over with other team members to find a solution. Being on the lookout for improvement keeps your skills sharp and helps make your campus more responsive to your students and staff.

Continuous Learning

A dedication to continuous learning should come easily to those who have committed themselves to working with

Key Principles to Building a Service Culture
• Focus on the customer.
• Get involved in the solution.
• Anticipate needs.
• Practice continuous learning.

higher education. You work with people every day who are striving to better themselves through learning. You can help them more effectively if you make the same commitment.

Delivering quality service requires knowing more than just your own corner of your institution. It requires knowledge of the big picture. Knowing where your office fits and how the institution works as a whole is vital to providing your customers with the information they need.

Learning about your institution will also make you a better team member when working with internal customers. Having the knowledge to help solve problems your co-workers may be experiencing helps you work more smoothly together and adds to your team effort of providing the best service.

Putting It All Together

You've covered the main principles of building a service culture in your campus community. Together these principles can help you perform your roles more effectively. Keeping the customer in mind, getting actively involved and committing yourself to continuous learning will help you serve your customers better, anticipate their needs more quickly, work efficiently as a team member and function better in your relationship with other departments.

By putting all the quality service principles together, you can improve your service to those you work with and help. Each step toward building a service culture makes being at your campus a more positive experience for everyone. Working together, you can achieve the level of excellence that is fitting for a quality institution.

Practical Approaches to Building a Service Culture

Discover Customer Requirements

Quality service begins with identifying what students and other customers want and what they need. Some people call these customer requirements. For example, you may learn that many students want to register for classes by phone and thus avoid long lines on registration day. A requirement for faculty might be to have textbook orders filled on time and accurately. For the staff in the registrar's office, a requirement might be to have all faculty grade reports turned in accurately and by the date due.

In other words, customer requirements are those things you identify as being important or necessary to customers. You will find that these requirements vary a great deal from group to group. Providing quality service means knowing your audience. What do traditional-age freshmen want and need? Traditional-age transfers? Nontraditional students? Minority students? Underprepared students? The better you are able to answer these questions, the better you will be able to provide high-quality service that meets the actual needs of students and other customers.

Develop Service Standards That Promote Excellence

Next, you'll create service standards designed to meet customer requirements and that help you measure whether or not you are meeting them. Service standards can be helpful for staff, administrators and faculty. Some standards are most effective when they become office policy and are expected to be followed regularly. For instance, an academic department might commit to complete transfer credit evaluations within a week. A registrar's office might expect that all transcript requests be processed and sent out within two days.

Other standards can be self-defined and can serve as important personal reminders of quality service that matters to the people you serve. An academic department probably would not want to set standards for what faculty do in the classroom. But this does not mean that individual faculty members can't devise standards for their own behavior. For instance, a faculty member might make a personal commitment to return every test or major paper to students within a week of receiving them, or to read every student's advising folder before each scheduled advising appointment, or to learn each student's name by the end of the second week of class.

These kinds of service standards are important for two reasons. First, they encourage you to focus on your customers and to actively seek to learn what's important to them. Second, standards almost always lead to better service and more satisfied customers.

Design Service Strategies That Work

Now that you know what you're aiming for, you can establish procedures or strategies for meeting the standards you have set for yourself or for your office. Note that the standards come before the strategies because the strategies sometimes require devising new systems or taking new approaches to your own work or the work of your office. For instance, getting out transcript requests within two days may necessitate new systems, policies or procedures.

Deliver Quality Service Through Every Contact

When the standards and strategies are in place, it's everyone's job to assure that they are used consistently and effectively in the thousands of large and small daily interactions a college or university has with its customers.

Check for Satisfaction

Finally, it's important to check for customer satisfaction to see if your standards and strategies are working. This can involve something as simple and informal as talking with customers and getting input from staff, administrators or faculty. In other cases, you may want to gather more formal feedback from paper-and-pencil surveys such as student satisfaction inventories or alumni surveys. You'll hear a lot more in Session Two about ways to check for satisfaction.

But, wait, you're not finished! The service culture model is really a loop rather than a linear progression. It starts with customer requirements and moves through checking for satisfaction. Then, after you check for satisfaction, you can apply what you've learned to re-define your customers' requirements as needed —and the entire process starts again.

Think of it this way:

- *Quality service skills* that you develop fit into the delivery part of the model. This is where individual excellence brings the service culture alive through every contact with internal and external customers.

- *Standards*, such as "cut the time from application to acceptance by one-third," are your guiding principles.

- *Customer requirements* are those things you'll begin to learn by keeping your focus on the customer.

An institution with a strong service culture is *obsessed* with excelling at every stage of this model. Service providers

Strategies for Individual Excellence

- Take every person and his or her concerns seriously.

- Give each person your full attention.

- Remember that in every contact you represent the institution.

- Take pride in your work.

- Enjoy your work — and show people that you do.

- Make people feel that you're happy to serve them.

- Remember that your work is part of a grand and noble enterprise—helping students to learn and grow and to realize their dreams.

do everything they can to find what customers need, then they bend over backward to deliver that. It doesn't matter that they might never have done it that way before.

An obsession with excellence means that everyone on the service team pushes to achieve his or her potential. The team judges its results against the very highest standards —average or "acceptable" results are never good enough.

What Customer-Focus *Really* Means

The service culture model presented here begins and ends with customer requirements. And what that really means, in the end, is a whole new way of viewing your work.

Operating within a service culture means viewing your role and your entire organization in new and creative ways. It means listening to your customers, visualizing the most outstanding service you could provide, then finding ways to turn that ideal into reality.

As you can see, it all begins and ends with customer requirements. Requirements are the driving force behind all of your service efforts, because only by meeting requirements can you build and sustain a service culture.

Points to Remember

- Quality service delivery begins and ends with customer requirements.

- Quality service means doing *everything you can*—and then some—to make sure your customers get what they need.

- An institution with a strong service culture is obsessed with excellence.

- A customer's requirements become his or her expectations of service.

Exercise 4: Applying Service Culture Principles

Question 1) In your own work what are examples of situations where you or your office need to understand and anticipate the needs of students, parents or other external customers?

Question 2) What are examples of situations where you or your office need to understand and anticipate the needs of staff, faculty and internal customers?

Question 3) How do your efforts to understand and anticipate needs make your own work easier?

Question 4) What methods can you use to understand and anticipate needs?

Optional Activity: Self-Assessment of Orientation and Training

The following six questions concern how you were oriented and trained when you first started work at this institution. Your answers to these questions can help the institution better meet the needs of staff, administrators and faculty when they first join the institution.

Question 1) How well do you think you were oriented and trained to your office or work area?

Question 2) What was missing, if anything, in the way you were oriented and trained to your office or work area?

Question 3) How well do you think you were oriented and trained to the institution as a whole?

Question 4) What was missing, if anything, in the way you were oriented and trained to the institution as a whole?

Question 5) What opportunities do you have for continuous learning in your work now?

Question 6) What opportunities would you like to have for continuous learning in your work that you don't have now?

Optional Follow-up Activity: Requirements, Standards and Strategies

Now that you've learned something about customer requirements, service standards and strategies, it's time to apply them to your own work.

Question 1) What are several requirements of the customers you work with?

Question 2) What strategies have you devised or could you devise to meet these requirements?

Question 3) What service standards *have* you developed to meet these requirements?

Question 4) What service standards *could* you develop to meet these requirements?

SECTION 5: Barriers to Effective Teamwork

Behind every delivery of service to an external customer are many supporting acts of service among internal customers.

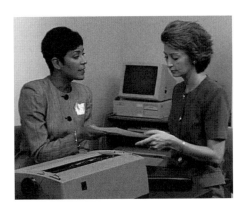

Each person must accept responsibility for performing his or her part of the service function with the highest quality possible. When that happens, service relationships are strengthened among co-workers and the external customer is delighted with your customer service.

Because you and other staff members are so closely linked in your efforts to serve your customers, you already belong—whether you realize it or not—to a service team. Like any team, you share common goals as well as agreed-upon procedures and strategies for reaching those goals. Common goals, such as improving student recruitment and student retention, help to build teams and promote teamwork.

Like any team, you've probably noticed changes in your service relationships. As you work harder to satisfy the customer's needs, you frequently update procedures and re-configure the ways in which you work together.

Sometimes these changes don't come easily. Staff members get frustrated with each other, with the system and even with the customer. You may occasionally hear someone mutter under her breath, "It sure was a lot easier when I did this whole process by myself." All of these are natural symptoms of the growing pains your team must face.

Barriers to Effective Teamwork

While it's true that you can accomplish more with a team than you can on your own, it's also true that there is a cost for that extra achievement. Teams never happen effortlessly. Teamwork, like a good marriage, requires conscious effort and a willingness to recognize, then handle, stumbling blocks.

Here are some of the most common barriers that threaten a team's success:

- Lack of commitment to common goals
- Shirking of responsibility by individual team members
- Communication gaps and breakdowns
- Information not freely or widely shared
- A climate of distrust
- Lack of support of decisions made by and for the team
- Fear of conflict or inappropriate conflict-resolution strategies
- Inattention to team process as well as to team tasks and results

Teamwork is critical to building a service culture and reaching your goals of excellence. In a varied and diversified institution, barriers to teamwork arise naturally, and sometimes working as a team can be difficult. Overcoming the barriers to effective teamwork takes individual commitment as well as a well-coordinated, team approach.

Before you look at how to work effectively as a team, take a look at some of the barriers that can keep you and your colleagues from performing as a team.

Conflicting Goals

Sharing similar goals is crucial to working efficiently together. A popular example of teamwork is the relay race team. The relay team can't win if each runner has a different idea about where the finish line is. In fact, they end up running in opposite directions.

Clearly stating goals at the start of a project and continuously checking where you are headed help you build on each other's work and reach your goals faster and easier. By communicating effectively with other team members, you can identify when you are working toward a common goal and when your goals are leading you in opposite directions.

Mission statements and service mission statements can be important reminders of institutional values and goals. Even though day-to-day priorities and activities may be very different among student affairs, academic affairs and administrative services, all three areas share key institutional goals such as student success and student retention. An important part of building a service culture is bringing individual and institutional goals in line with one another.

Communication Breakdowns

Everyone has experienced communication breakdowns. Gaps in the lines of communication can cause hours of frustration and extra work. Although it may be impossible to eliminate communication breakdowns completely from your system, you can significantly reduce them by maintaining your commitment to continuous learning. The more you know about how your system works, the more likely it is that you will recognize when a piece of information is missing before it inconveniences your customers.

Getting together to discuss things, even non-work-related topics, develops an atmosphere where communication is easier. Like anything else, you need to practice your communication.

Lack of Information

Withholding information makes some people feel valuable and important. However, when building a service culture, freely sharing information provides the mortar that holds together the building blocks of better communication and better service.

To see the importance of freely shared information, think of the differences between a college or university and almost any business. For instance, when you call or walk into a department store, a hotel or a restaurant, you likely will be served by or have contact with a very small number of people compared with the total number of employees and the number of "offices" within each business. When you travel by air to another city, you may have contact only with check-in desk personnel and flight attendants and have no contact with the pilots, baggage handlers or dozens of others who provide service to you indirectly. When dealing with a large corporation with thousands of employees, you may only have contact with a customer service representative in a customer service office.

In such tightly controlled settings, it is a much easier task to share up-to-date and accurate information. To use an analogy, imagine these businesses as a house with a front door. A customer comes to the front door and knocks. A service provider opens the door, stands in the doorway and helps her.

In contrast, imagine a college or university as a large house with many doorways on every side but none of them having a door. A student walks around the outside of the house until he decides which doorway to enter. He walks in the house and starts looking around. He sees people in the kitchen cooking, others paying bills at a messy desk, and he hears people talking on a phone upstairs. He calls out, "I'm looking for my advisor. Can you tell me if she's in today?"

Compared to almost any other kind of business or enterprise, colleges and universities present an almost completely transparent face to the public. In such an environment, the run-around is inevitable unless individuals and offices freely share information and train others how to use it.

Lack of Follow-Through

Your role in a quality service culture demands your responsibility to see things through. A lack of follow-through, or "dropping the ball," hurts everyone. It also denies you the feelings of satisfaction and accomplishment that go along with seeing a project to its completion or a problem to its resolution.

Earlier in the program you watched a prospective transfer student trudge from office to office in search of information about his transfer credits. Even though the admissions office and the history department did not have the specific information he needed, the offices could have followed through by making phone calls on the student's behalf to end the run-around.

Follow-through not only helps the customer, it also helps staff in other offices. Follow-through is not just an individual issue. It's a team issue. The fast pace of your institution may require the occasional "dropped ball," but through quality teamwork and good communication, you can rebound quickly and pick up a project where another has left off. Quality service means helping each other, your internal customers, as much as your external customers.

Lack of Trust

Next to withholding information, lack of trust is the major barrier to effective teamwork. As a team you need to have confidence in each other and trust each other to provide the support you need to perform at your highest level. You've seen earlier that conflicting goals can lead to poor service. Conflicting goals can also lead to lack of trust. It takes the supreme effort of everyone to reach beyond the divisions on campus to improve relationships and in turn improve your system. Reaching out can't be done without a basic level of trust.

Sometimes the issue of trust can be an issue of trusting yourself. Your own expectations of excellence may be so high that you feel no one else can do it "my way" and therefore you may as well do everything yourself. This way of thinking not only diminishes the quality of your work, it damages your relationships with others. Being able to trust yourself to deal with changes or differences in the work of others frees you to lighten your work load and helps build the confidence of the people you work with.

Unmanaged Conflict

You have all had the experience of being involved in a conflict with another person. You may have been tempted to let it go unresolved and ignore the person you have a conflict with. In a service culture, however, you have a responsibility to let your team members know how you feel.

Conflicts are a natural part of living and working to-gether. Instead of being avoided, conflicts should be welcomed as an opportunity to share opposing views and new ideas. When you open yourself up to conflict and talk about it, the conflict often has a way of working itself out and your life is enriched by the experience. When conflict enters your workplace, talk it out. You'll feel better and your team relationships will be strengthened.

Points to Remember

- Shared goals promote teamwork.

- Every person has a part to play in team-building.

- Teams never happen effortlessly. Teamwork requires conscious and continuing efforts.

- Naturally occurring barriers to teams are always present.

- Barriers to effective teamwork are best overcome through a team approach.

- Promoting good communication and sharing information freely are the best ways to overcome barriers.

Exercise 5: Identifying Barriers to Team Performance

Question 1) What are the barriers to team performance mentioned in the last video segment?

Question 2) Have you experienced other kinds of barriers that get in the way of team performance?

Optional Activity: What Teams Are You On?

As a staff member at your institution, you belong to several teams—the campuswide team, a team composed of all the staff members in your department or office, and a smaller team within your own work group or area. You may also consider yourself part of a team that includes several offices that work closely together, such as a student affairs division.

Each of these teams has a different kind of membership, different goals, and a unique way in which it supports the vision and mission of your institution.

Question 1) Do you consider yourself part of one or more teams? Why or why not?

Question 2) If you think of yourself as part of a team, how does that affect your work and your relationship with your colleagues?

Question 3) Do you see any of the teams you belong to as having different or conflicting goals from one another?

Question 4) What results from having different or conflicting goals?

SECTION 6: Overcoming Barriers to Team Performance

In the last section you discussed barriers to team performance and how to identify when something is interfering with your ability to serve your customers effectively. In this section, you will discuss ways to use creative problem solving to overcome barriers and find solutions to problems quickly.

Imagine the situation of a confused student coming into your office. She has been trying to find an office in another part of the building and is lost. If your office had a strong service team orientation, you would be able to show this student to the right office while a team member took over your duties temporarily. Helping others as a team enables you to deliver outstanding service.

Keys to Overcoming Barriers

To overcome barriers to effective teamwork, use the quality service approaches you have discussed so far in Advanced Connections:

- Keep focused on the customer.

- Get involved.

- Continue to learn.

- Get together often.

These approaches will help you troubleshoot through a problem with others.

"Keep focused on the customer" also means your internal customers—your fellow team members. It's just as important to respect them and their priorities as it is to respect external customers. In some organizations it is all too common for an idea to be rejected by one party simply because it comes from the opposing camp. Mutual respect is of utmost importance in creative problem solving.

Get involved. It has been said that if you're not part of the solution, you're part of the problem. Creative problem solving should involve everyone. No matter what your position or connection with a problem, trust your instincts and your ideas. They are valuable and foster more ideas.

Continue to learn. Expand your knowledge to include all aspects of a problem. The better you understand a situation the closer you are to a solution.

Working together effectively means being open to other ideas and respecting the priorities of your team members, even if they conflict with your own. By keeping an open mind and reminding yourself to respect the position of other people on your team, you can create an atmosphere where ideas are exchanged easily and problems are resolved quickly.

Get together often. It is difficult to feel like you're part of a team when you don't spend time with other team members. This is especially important when teams are made up of people who don't work in the same office. After big events such as orientation and registration, some colleges gather all the staff and managers involved in the event to discuss what went well, to identify problems and to start planning how to make it better the next time. When you get together, you will communicate better, understand each other's needs and feel more like a team.

Keeping Everyone Active

Have you ever noticed a problem, started to say something and then thought better of it? Perhaps you figured it was none of your business. Well, in a service culture, delivering quality service is everyone's business. Just because it's not your department or area of expertise doesn't mean you don't have interesting ideas to contribute.

To get the most out of problem solving, you have to keep everyone actively involved with finding a solution. You have to eliminate the "minding your own business" attitude and attack a problem from all sides. This includes seeking out the thoughts of others in your group who might not otherwise speak up. Working to make everyone feel included and keeping them active in the problem-solving process is every team member's responsibility.

Handling Disagreements

You may have already found that there are members of your team you don't always see eye-to-eye with. Although frustrating and discouraging at times, different points of view present opportunities for you to stretch your imagination. Finding a common ground or an acceptable solution to a problem that your team members disagree on pushes your skills to the limits and forces you to reach further for a solution.

Sometimes you are faced with problems that seem overwhelming to you. Through creative problem solving and getting everyone involved, you can turn barriers into opportunities to expand your learning and improve the system for everyone.

As an important member of your team, you have a powerful influence over how well your customers are served. One of the first ways to make sure your service is up to par is to make sure your team is operating smoothly and effectively.

Points to Remember

- Every staff member is a part of several service teams which are responsible for building the linkages, or relationships, among members.

- Each team member serves internal customers by performing a wide variety of tasks.

- Team members must work to overcome common barriers to team performance.

- Effective teams demonstrate commitment practice consensus, display care, communicate, and clearly understand goals and roles.

Exercise 6: Overcoming Barriers to Team Performance

Question 1) If you were involved in the situation in the music department, how might you prevent the problem from happening in the future?

Question 2) What are some examples of bureaucracy and red tape in your work area that could be reduced or eliminated?

Question 3) What are some examples of bureaucracy and red tape in other parts of your institution that you would like to see reduced or eliminated?

Question 4) Earlier you identified several common barriers to team performance. Keeping in mind what you've learned about teamwork, use the columns below to note the ideas you have on how to overcome those barriers.

Barrier   **Possible Solution**

Conflicting goals   _____

                                         _____

                                         _____

Communication
breakdowns   _____

                                         _____

                                         _____

Information hoarding
or turf protection   _____

                                         _____

                                         _____

Lack of follow-through   _____

                                         _____

                                         _____

Lack of trust   _____

                                         _____

                                         _____

Unmanaged conflict   _____

                                         _____

                                         _____

SECTION 7: Characteristics of the Best Team Players

You want to be the best team member you can be. Not only will this help you serve your customers, it will improve your relationship with other team members. Identifying characteristics that good team players possess is the first step to becoming a better team player yourself.

Understanding Needs

Understanding as much as you can about the system you work in and the systems others at your institution work in is a crucial responsibility of any good team player. It not only helps solve problems, but it enables you to anticipate the needs of others and provide service beyond their expectations.

Imagine that you work in the registrar's office, and you receive a phone call from a student. He would like to drop a gym class and add a dance class. He may be asking only for the hours that your office is open, but by understanding your system you also remind him to bring his student I.D. with him and to be sure to have his drop/add slip signed.

The next call is from a new faculty member. He is unsure about the dates when students can no longer add or drop classes. You verify the dates, but you sense that he has another question. You elaborate and explain that a student who wishes to add a class after the deadline must get three signatures and submit a statement explaining the reasons for missing the deadline. Now the faculty member understands the *whole* situation. A student of his had asked him to sign a statement about missing a drop/add deadline and he was confused about what was going on.

Continuous learning goes hand-in-hand with continuous teaching. If you sense that someone may not understand your procedures fully, offer to explain them. Even if a fellow team member seems familiar with your work, refreshing their knowledge or elaborating on a detail with a brief explanation can help focus on a problem and help you reach a solution quickly.

Timeliness

Have you ever been frustrated by the service at a fast food restaurant? After all, they call themselves "fast" food, but you may end up waiting in line while the people behind the counter take forever to fill your order. Not only are you disappointed with the service, you also feel that your business is not valued.

Improving your skills to become a better team member will help you save time, but sometimes that is not enough. Providing service quickly and efficiently is also important. A quality team member lets customers know that serving them is not only important, but vital. Not everyone you come in contact with will be in a hurry, but acting promptly lets them know how important their needs are to you.

Problem Solving

A quality service team member is always interested in working with others to make everyone's job easier. Using your skills at problem solving helps you overcome obstacles and work together more efficiently. It empowers those you work with.

An angry parent calls your office. Her daughter has been mistakenly left off the dean's list. You calm the angry parent and promise to look into the matter. You then get together with your team members and discuss ways to make up for the mistakes in the current list. Taking out an ad in the school newspaper, reprinting the list and writing personal notes of apology are all considered. But you don't stop there. You also discuss creating a system for determining dean's list students that includes an additional set of checks to prevent future errors.

Using a team approach to solve problems encourages the best aspects of a service culture: keeping lines of communication open, trusting each other and making sure everyone is actively participating in achieving shared goals.

> ### Keys to Effective Team-Building
>
> - Talk frequently about shared goals.
>
> - Help staff remember how his or her work fits into the "big picture."
>
> - Establish an open environment for sharing ideas and feelings.
>
> - Focus on continuous learning.
>
> - Get together often.
>
> - Communicate concerns.
>
> - Celebrate successes.

Commitment to Quality

If a restaurant or clothing store (or almost any other type of business) makes a mistake, the customer may be inconvenienced, but rarely is there any long-term damage. If you are served the wrong entree, the restaurant will bring you another at no charge. If you buy a suit that is defective or poorly made, the clothing store will replace it. You may even receive a monetary credit toward your next purchase.

In colleges and universities, as with health care providers, quality matters in different ways than in most businesses. Colleges and universities make mistakes every day that cost students thousands of dollars in wasted tuition, cost students jobs and drive prospective students away. Consider these examples. A student is misadvised and has to graduate a year late because the required course she did not take is only offered once a year. The registrar's office makes a mistake on a student's graduation analysis and notifies the student a month before graduation that he doesn't have all his general education requirements satisfied. The Educational Placement Office misplaces a dossier request and costs a recent graduate a teaching job. The Admissions Office misfiles an incoming transcript for an applied student. The file is never acted on, and the student ends up enrolling elsewhere.

Quality matters. Often in higher education there are no second chances, no opportunities to undo damaging mistakes. Work has to be done right the first time. Teamwork promotes better cooperation and better communication. These, in turn, lead to fewer mistakes. That helps everyone.

Many companies have soared over their competition through a renewed commitment to quality, an emphasis on training and development, and a focus on team building and organizational development. In similar ways, many colleges and universities have dramatically improved student recruitment and retention by improving the quality of education, focusing on staff and faculty development and using strategic planning to change the institution and the way it operates.

Positive Attitude

No one expects you to be happy all the time, but a good team member makes a constant effort to approach each situation with an open mind and a positive outlook. Feeling that you can be of service is the first step to delivering that service.

If team members are confident that they can handle any

problem, coming to a solution is easier. You need attitudes that say, "I can't wait to hear what they think about my idea," and "Thank goodness we've got such a talented group to tackle this problem." A positive attitude gives you power and makes things seem easy, while a negative outlook robs you of confidence and energy.

In the next session you will explore some of the ways you can develop the characteristics that will make you a better team member.

Points to Remember

- Teamwork is essential to building a service culture.

- Teams are built by and need individuals who understand customer needs, who take an active role in solving problems and who believe that quality matters.

- A team approach makes work easier and more enjoyable.

- Some teams are made up of people from the same office. Other teams are made up of people who share processes or events such as student orientation or registration.

Exercise 7: Ideas for Individual and Team Improvement

Question 1) How would you rate your individual characteristics as a team member? For each item, circle the number that best fits your personal characteristics (6 is high, 1 is low).

Personal Characteristics	Personal Rating
1. Understanding needs	6 5 4 3 2 1
2. Timeliness	6 5 4 3 2 1
3. Problem solving	6 5 4 3 2 1
4. Commitment to quality	6 5 4 3 2 1
5. Positive attitude	6 5 4 3 2 1
6. Knowledge of work area	6 5 4 3 2 1
7. Knowledge of institution	6 5 4 3 2 1
8. Commitment to continuous learning	6 5 4 3 2 1

Question 2) Take a look at your immediate work group. How well do you function as a team? Are there barriers in place that you need to overcome? Have you seen areas where you yourself could improve?

Question 3) Do you see areas for improvement within your own department? How could you perform more effectively as a team?

Question 4) Finally, which skills do you think you as a campus team could work on?

My Commitment to Self-Development

As a result of what I've learned today, I am making a commitment to work toward improvement in these areas:

1. _____

2. _____

3. _____

4. _____

5. _____

6. _____

7. _____

I will ask _____ to help me check my
　　　　　　　(Co-worker's name)

progress on _____.
　　　　　　　　(Date)

SESSION TWO: Polishing Daily Service Skills —————————

SECTION 1: Introduction

Welcome to the second session of Advanced Connections! In the first session you discussed aspects of building a service culture and your role in creating a service culture in your campus community. In the second session, you will discuss and practice skills that can be used daily to help build a service culture and develop relationships with internal and external customers.

Think of a skill or talent you have worked to develop. Maybe it was dancing, or a craft like woodworking, or even a business skill, such as letter writing or making speeches. In all your endeavors, if you want to excel at something, you have to practice. That's what this session is all about; it shows you how individual practice fits into the bigger picture.

Building a service culture is not a task you finish and then leave behind as you move on to something else. A service culture grows and develops as more and more individual service providers practice and perfect the daily skills that promote service excellence. A service culture also grows through an institution's efforts to identify and eliminate institutional roadblocks to service excellence. Session Two explores both of these elements.

Session One presented a series of practical approaches to building a service culture:

1. Discover customer requirements.
2. Develop service standards that promote excellence.
3. Design strategies that work.
4. Deliver quality service through every contact.
5. Check for satisfaction.

Session Two provides the opportunity to see how all these approaches work together. You will:

1. Take the time to practice some of the daily skills necessary to "deliver quality service through every contact."
2. Talk about some of the service standards and strategies that promote excellence in these daily skills.
3. Focus on techniques for checking for satisfaction on an individual, departmental and institutional level.

Here are examples of how it all works together. Sections 4 and 5 of Session Two focus on two topics that are key to reducing the phone run-around on campus. In these sections, staff learn the most effective skills for handling calls and reducing needless transfers. In turn, administrators focus on their role—working with staff to develop service standards and strategies to improve phone service, and working with other offices on campus to tackle interdepartmental or campuswide issues.

If you are an administrator or supervisor, Session Two will help you in your role as service role model and mentor. To improve the overall level of service and work to build a service culture, you need to model your best daily work skills with internal and external customers. This session gives you a common language with which to discuss service standards and expectations with staff. In addition, to maintain service at a high level, you need to be able to teach service skills and expectations to new employees as well as reinforce the daily use of these skills through staff meetings and other training opportunities in your office or work area.

Session Two will help you and your institution put it all together.

> **Keys to Effective Personal Communication**
>
> - Be enthusiastic.
> - Be attentive.
> - Stay focused on the customer.

Session Two Topics

Practicing face-to-face skills. This session will help you evaluate your face-to-face communication and help you improve your skills.

Uncovering customer needs. As you discussed in Session One, understanding needs is the first and most crucial step to delivering quality service. Sometimes customers are not fully aware of what they need to know. This session provides an opportunity to learn about and practice techniques to uncover customer needs.

Using the telephone to advantage. Without eye contact, and other nonverbal communication to rely on, telephone conversation is a misunderstanding waiting to happen. In this section you'll explore ways to make your intentions and information understood clearly.

Mastering call transfers and messages. This session will help you master advanced call transfer, screening and message taking techniques. You will also focus on ways to reduce the number of needless phone transfers campuswide.

Checking for customer satisfaction. In this section, you will practice techniques of checking for satisfaction, so you can be sure that you are meeting customer needs.

Effective Personal Communication

Communication skills are important for success in both your professional and your personal lives. Because you communicate with others all day long, the tendency is to believe that you're "practicing" communication skills all the time. But are you really communicating?

- *Talking* isn't the same as *getting your message across.*

- *Hearing* what someone tells you isn't the same as truly *listening* to the verbal and nonverbal signals sent by the speaker.

When it comes to delivering quality customer service and nurturing service relationships, there's no substitute for outstanding communication skills.

Advanced speaking skills help you to:

- Ask for the customer's expectations.

- Explain service solutions.

- Apologize for service problems.

- Show appreciation for the efforts of others on your service team.

Meanwhile, advanced listening skills help you to:

- Uncover and interpret customer needs.

- Learn customer expectations.

- Communicate your interest and concern for customer needs.

First Impressions Are Lasting Impressions

Customers frequently gain their first impression of your institution based on the service provider's communication skills. Then, during every contact thereafter, the manner in which you communicate continues to make further impressions.

Average communication skills tend to cover the facts, but often don't convey your professional, service-oriented attitude. Advanced communication skills put that extra polish on your service relationships—the icing on the cake that makes your customers want to come back for more!

Which kind of communication makes the best impression on you?

Average Communication	Advanced Communication
"Yes?"	"How may I help you?"
"You're welcome."	"You're quite welcome— I'm happy to help!"
"Yes, I remember you."	"Sure I remember you— it's good to see you again!"

Of course, there's nothing technically *wrong* with the approaches in the left column. Yet, don't you agree that the communications on the right project a stronger service attitude?

Your communication skills constantly advertise your service attitudes and abilities to your customers. This includes internal customers, too, who shouldn't be taken for granted just because they're "like family."

Offices Make First Impressions Too

First impressions are just as important in offices as they are for individuals. Think about the first impression your office makes with respect to the work your office does, the way you interact with customers, and the needs and interests of your customers.

If your office serves students, parents or other visitors, you'll want to make your office as inviting as possible. Here are just a few tips to help your office be more welcoming and make a better first impression:

- Be sure your office hours match the needs of your customers.

- Be sure people can find you. Check for adequate signage outside your building, at the major entrances of the building, and outside your office door.

- If practical, keep your main entrance door open during business hours so that customers know they are welcome and expected.

- If you need to keep your main entrance door closed, post a simple greeting on the door, such as "Welcome to the Financial Aid Office. Please come in."

- If students need to discuss sensitive topics such as grades, family finances or financial aid, be sure to provide a private area in your office for these interactions.

- Provide a waiting area and refreshments for students waiting to be helped. Think about offering them something to do if they must stand in line. If students often need to wait a long time to be helped, provide a large enough waiting area for them to sit down. One business office with chronically long lines installed a TV in the waiting area. Such strategies may be the best immediate approach, but the best long-term solution is to *reduce or eliminate the need for students to stand in line in the first place.*

- For young children provide a place to sit and play quietly and/or some age-specific materials such as coloring books and crayons, books for young readers and nonreaders, etc.

- Decorate your office in ways that support and complement the image your institution is trying to convey.

- Avoid using voice mail or automated attendant to answer the main number for an office during business hours.

Roadblocks to Communication

Communicating seems easy, until you consider all the barriers that can cause breakdowns along the way. When what you think you said is different from what the other person thinks they heard, one of these roadblocks may be the culprit.

Perhaps the speaker—

- Spoke in jargon. *Strategy:* Use words and phrases geared to the listener's background and experience level.

- Used distracting mannerisms. *Strategy:* Make it easy for listeners to pay attention to the core of your message.

- Assumed a common frame of reference. *Strategy:* Remember that your experience is unique to you, so the meanings you place on words may be slightly different from someone else's. Check frequently for understanding.

- Monopolized the conversation. *Strategy:* Give listeners an opportunity to respond and ask questions.

- Sent conflicting messages. *Strategy:* Communicate openly and honestly, using words, tones and gestures that complement rather than conflict with each other.

Perhaps the listener—

- Made assumptions about what the speaker was going to say. *Strategy:* Listen for the real message, not the one that fits your preconceived notions.

- Succumbed to distractions. *Strategy:* Tune out what's going on around you and concentrate on the speaker's message.

- Spent time rehearsing a response. *Strategy:* Resist the temptation to mull over what you'll say next rather than listen.

Communication Skills I'd Like to Develop

Based on the discussions so far in the program, and looking back on my own experiences, these are some of the communication skills I'd like to develop:

- Skill: _____

   Things I can do to improve:_____

   _____

   _____

- Skill: _____

   Things I can do to improve:_____

   _____

   _____

- Skill: _____

   Things I can do to improve:_____

   _____

   _____

Points to Remember

- The keys to effective communication are: be enthusiastic, be attentive and stay focused on the customer.

- Advanced communication skills are the foundation for delivering quality service.

- Both the sender and the receiver can experience communication roadblocks that alter the message.

- Offices, as well as people, make first impressions.

Exercise 8: Positive Face-to-Face Communication

Question 1) What are the keys to effective communication presented in the last video segment?

Question 2) Look at the first one—being enthusiastic. What can you do in your work life to make that happen?

Question 3) What can you do in your work life to assure that you are attentive and focused on the customer?

Question 4) What are some of the obstacles that get in the way of positive, face-to-face communication in your office?

Question 5) How do you overcome some of these obstacles to effective communication?

Question 6) The last video segment discusses first impressions. If your office serves external customers, what kind of first impression does it make?

Question 7) Does the first impression of your office match the service culture you are trying to build?

SECTION 2: Advanced Face-to-Face Communication

Everyone is familiar with nonverbal cues. Children often aggravate their siblings or parents by refusing to read their nonverbal cues and taking them only at word value. For instance, a parent tells a child to stay in bed by saying, "Keep your head on your pillow." As soon as the parent's back is turned, the child sits up, places the pillow on his or her head and proceeds to get out of bed.

A stern look, a definite tone of voice, a pointing finger— all these nonverbal signals tell the child to lie down and go to sleep. By purposely ignoring everything but the verbal cues, the child demonstrates how easy it is to misunderstand someone when you depend only on what is said.

Body Language

Facial expression, eye contact, posture, handshake or the way you walk all are cues that tell others about who you are before you even begin to speak. Being aware of what your body language is saying is the first step towards using it as a tool to deliver quality service.

Use a mirror or have a friend give you insights into how you present yourself to others. Once you are aware of what your body language is telling people, you can use it to help your customers more effectively.

Tone of Voice

If you've ever had a pet, you know that the tone of voice you use to talk to them contains all the meaning. Regardless of what your words say, a dog feels praised if you use a soothing tone of voice.

Listening to a student's tone of voice can help you understand what she wants as well. She may be asking a simple question, but from her exasperated manner, you sense she needs something else. Perhaps she has been trying to get information about enrolling in a graduate program, but has become so fed up with a run-around, she is now only asking for directions.

Spatial Relationships

On a crowded bus the person next to you sits so close he is almost on your lap. Are you insulted? Do you feel threatened? No, because you understand that the bus is packed full of people and there is no room. How would you feel if the bus was almost empty and the person sat that close?

Spatial relationships can be very important in how you feel about the people and situations you are dealing with. Often you aren't even aware when you respond to a spatial relationship. You automatically back up from someone who has invaded your personal space. You naturally lean forward when listening to something that interests you.

Paying special attention to your customers' spatial cues and preferences makes it easier for you to help them. As you approach a student entering your office he seems to back away from you. Because you are aware of spatial relationships you offer the student a chair and leave plenty of room between you. Suddenly his shy manner gives way and he begins to give you complete details about the information he needs.

Prevent Customer Mistakes

Just as you may sometimes misunderstand your customers, so may they misunderstand you. You can prevent most customer mistakes by reading your customers' nonverbal cues and using your own verbal and nonverbal messages to make yourself better understood.

Make Your Point Clearly

Have you ever handed a cup of hot chocolate to a small child? If you have, then you know that you don't simply give it to them. You carefully set it down away from him and tell him repeatedly to "be careful" because "it's HOT!" You may even demonstrate how he can blow gently on it until it is cool enough to drink. Through tone of voice, body language and spatial relationships you make your point clearly.

Usually it is not necessary to be as deliberate when dealing with adults, but by using the same techniques you can let your customers know what is important. For example, when giving a customer a form to fill out you may mention an important part, such as the signature, several times.

Check Up on Yourself

No one likes to work in a vacuum. You want to know when you do a good job, and you like to feel that you are effective and that you make a difference. Developing skills to help you assess your service will give you this satisfaction.

"Anything else I can do for you?" "Everything okay?" "Is this what you need?" By asking students and other customers for their input you can verify that your service is on the right track. Asking questions is also one of the easiest ways to predict a customer's needs.

ADMINISTRATOR: Anything else I can do for you?

STUDENT: Nope. I'm just going to take these over to the financial aid office.

ADMINISTRATOR: Okay. That office is down the hall and through the double doors.

STUDENT: Thanks!

Asking questions about your service can help you assess your effectiveness and make you more effective by helping you understand your customers and their needs better.

Reading Customer Cues

Outstanding service providers look for cues that lead them in meeting the student's needs and exceeding expectations.

Some cues are so obvious you can't miss them. The student may—

- Ask for extra help completing a registration form.

- Stand in the middle of the room, looking lost.

- Laugh out loud when you say parking will be no problem.

In all of these situations, it's easy to see that some customer-centered communicating is in order.

Other cues, however, are much less obvious. Maybe a single word muttered dejectedly—"Oh"—or a fleeting glance at others in line indicates more privacy is desired.

Why Customers Give Subtle Cues

Think about your own experiences as a customer:

- Maybe you're in a shoe store, and every pair you're shown is too expensive for your budget. When the salesperson enthusiastically asks which pair you'll purchase, you mumble, "Umm ... I don't know ... uh, I think maybe I won't buy any shoes today after all."

- Or, you're on a trip and you ask for directions from a hotel employee. She gives a curt, quick jumble of street names and landmarks, then concludes with a perfunctory, "Got it?" You just stare at her for a second, then say, "Yeah, thanks," and start looking for someone else to ask.

In both of these instances, you gave subtle cues to the service provider that all was not well. The perceptive provider would have noticed a change in your tone, a hesitation, a choice of words that was less than positive.

Why didn't you come right out and ask for what you wanted? Because, for whatever reason, you didn't feel comfortable enough to do so. The same thing happens on campus.

Students and other customers you serve may feel uncomfortable, and therefore give only subtle cues, because they—

- Don't understand the system and feel inadequate. This is a classic problem for incoming new students who find themselves in a new and unfamiliar world.

- Feel confused, and are still trying to process in their own minds what the problem is.

- Get the impression that you don't have the time—or perhaps the patience —to deal with their problem.

For whatever reason, the customer is consciously or subconsciously holding back—censoring the conversation in an effort to be "acceptable" or "polite" or "no trouble."

Of course, as a person dedicated to quality service, you *want* to know what's on the customer's mind. When you pick up on a subtle cue, ask about it in a friendly way, and then solve the problem. After that, you'll have given that customer "permission" to be more forthright about other issues. In time, you can actually train most of your repeat customers to be open with you about their needs!

Points to Remember

- Be sensitive to the situation when reading your customer for cues.

- Customers give obvious cues to their needs when they feel comfortable doing so, and more subtle cues when they are "holding back."

- Effective communication can prevent many customer "mistakes."

- Reading cues to both needs and feelings is important to overall customer satisfaction.

Exercise 9: Connecting Customer Cues to Customer Needs and Feelings

Question 1) In the video scene with the nontraditional student, what was she really asking for help with?

Question 2) What cues was the nontraditional student giving?

Question 3) The last video segment suggested that sometimes you have to go beyond the questions customers ask to discover what they really want or need. What are examples of this in your own work area?

Question 4) The video also suggests that telling is not communicating. Can you think of any examples from your work when customers aren't getting the messages you're communicating? Why do you think this happens? What could you do to ensure better communication?

Exercise 10: Preventing Common Customer Mistakes

In the first column below, write down several examples of common mistakes made by students, faculty and administrators at your institution. In the second column write down ways to prevent these mistakes.

Common Customer Mistakes	Prevention Techniques
Students: _____	_____
_____	_____
_____	_____
Faculty: _____	_____
_____	_____
_____	_____
Administrators/staff: _____	_____
_____	_____
_____	_____

SECTION 3: Effective Personal Communication on the Telephone

I n the last section you saw how important visual cues are to making yourself understood. On the telephone, visual cues are gone and you have to rely only on your verbal skills. This means using your best listening, speaking and questioning skills to help your customers effectively and efficiently.

You already have good basic telephone skills. In this section you will cover some techniques and exercises to improve your skills and increase your effectiveness over the phone.

Lend an Ear

Listening is one of the most important skills you need to possess. Your customers may not give you the whole story. Listening between the words—like reading between the lines—is sometimes tricky, but it can really help give you a better idea of what your customers need.

Think about the times you give verbal cues about your feelings to someone on the phone. Maybe it is a co-worker who calls you right in the middle of dinner. You are polite and courteous, but the caller senses that you do not want to talk. He asks if he has interrupted something. How does he know? Perhaps he picks up on your short responses or an awkward pause. The caller uses careful listening techniques to be sensitive to the cues you give. The caller uses what he knows about you to heighten his awareness of your verbal cues.

Even if you've never met the people you call, you can use the same techniques to help understand your customers.

Take People Seriously

In the first session you learned one of the key strategies for individual excellence: take people and their concerns seriously. Most people have the skills they need to read cues *when they want to*. In the example of the co-worker who called you during dinner, the caller listened to your cues and was sensitive to them because the caller took you seriously. The caller took you seriously because you are important to him.

Everyone has had experiences with telemarketers who call during dinner and just barge ahead with their end of the conversation while ignoring every cue you give of your impatience and disinterest. When this happens, the telemarketer is not sensitive to you and your situation because he doesn't care about you. He is focused on himself and the possibility of making another sale. In other words, he doesn't take you seriously.

Here is another example. A student stops his faculty advisor to ask a question when the advisor is on his way to teach a class. If the advisor keeps walking and says to the student, "I don't have time to talk now, I have to teach a class," the advisor is not taking the student seriously. The advisor could stop very briefly, look the student directly in the eye and say, "I'd like to talk with you but I can't right now. Can you call or come by my office later today?" That comment says to the student, "I take you and your concerns seriously, and I want to help you."

Advanced Connections teaches many skills and strategies to provide better service, but they work only when you make the effort to take people seriously. Taking people seriously means paying full attention to them, really listening to them and caring about their problems and concerns, no matter how large or small.

Ask and Invite Questions

Your listening and speaking techniques will help you provide better service to your customers. Asking the right questions can improve your service even more. Questions help you clarify issues and can also help ensure that you are giving the most complete service possible.

Colleges and universities can be strange and complicated places, especially for students and parents new to higher education. Asking questions is especially important in serving students and other customers who may not know what questions to ask *you*.

> ## Take People Seriously in Every Service Contact
>
> Taking people seriously means paying full attention to them, really listening to them and caring about their problems and concerns, no matter how large or small.
>
> It is easy to take people seriously if they are important to you and if you know and care about them.
>
> Quality service professionals train themselves to take people seriously in every service contact.

When students don't ask questions or speak up in class, inexperienced teachers often assume that students understand the material being presented. In contrast, experienced teachers know that when students don't speak up, it often means they don't know what to ask, or they may be reluctant to ask questions out of fear or shyness. Experienced classroom teachers frequently check for understanding and invite comments and questions with statements such as, "Do you see the connection between such and such?" "Is this making sense to you?" or "Is it clear what the writer is saying here?"

Experienced service providers frequently ask questions to check for understanding, to uncover feelings and expectations, and to prevent future problems and confusion. So, when someone asks you where the campus parking office is, don't say something like, "It's on the ground floor of the Union ramp." Instead, start with a question such as, "Are you familiar with the campus?" The person's response to that question will dictate your next step. For someone familiar with campus, a simple description of location will suffice. A person new to campus may need detailed directions and may even need to look at a map.

Sometimes the best way to check for understanding and to invite questions is to ask your customers to complete forms (or start completing them) in your office. Many people learn best by doing. You can explain a form or a procedure to someone at length, but he may not really understand it until he sits down to do it. That's when questions arise. The next time you hand a form to someone, try saying, "If you have a few minutes, you might want to start completing that form in the office so we can answer any questions you might have." Using that approach can help you *and* the customer avoid dealing with problems and mistakes. Asking and inviting questions makes first-class service easier to deliver.

Telephone Techniques That Get Results

For all its advantages, sometimes the way in which you use the telephone can actually *hamper* communications. Here's how.

- The telephone is an auditory medium. Gestures, facial expressions and body language are taken out of the equation. What you say and how you say it are the only cues your listener has to understand what you really mean.

- The telephone is solitary. Each caller is free to daydream, doodle, write a letter or carry on a silent conversation with someone on the side—while the person on the other end will never know why communication has broken down.

Fortunately there are solutions to these shortcomings if you follow the keys to effective communication: 1) be enthusiastic, 2) be attentive, and 3) stay focused on the customer.

Say the Word

Pay special attention to how you sound on the phone. This is crucial because your tone must convey all the information that your nonverbal body language normally would.

Your "normal" tone of voice is probably not enough to make a good impression on your callers. Telephone experts recommend that you literally smile as you talk—it will noticeably improve your tone.

> ### Give Callers Your Full Attention
>
> To assure that customers get your full attention over the phone, try these techniques:
>
> - Turn away from your keyboard or desk. Turn away from your paperwork.
>
> - Don't read anything. Put down your pen except to take notes.
>
> - Don't look at or talk to other people.
>
> - Remove any distractions that take away from your full attention.

Whenever you speak over the phone, imagine that you're walking onto a theater stage. Just as actors wear make-up, make large gestures and raise their volume—enhancements that are necessary for reaching the whole audience—so too must you enhance your voice a few notches when speaking on the telephone.

Tips for Improving Your Telephone Manner

Each time you talk over the telephone, remember to:

- Answer calls promptly, by the second or third ring.

- Assume your "telephone voice" by controlling your volume and speed and enhancing your tone.

- Use the caller's name during the conversation.

- Avoid eating or drinking while on the phone.

- Re-dial if the connection is poor.

- Project a tone that is cheerful, natural, attentive and respectful.

- When problems occur, project a tone which is concerned, sympathetic and apologetic.

- Speak calmly and choose your words naturally.

- Use your listening skills, and re-state all important information to check understanding and accuracy.

- Avoid interruptions and, when they can't be avoided, apologize to the caller.

- End the conversation with agreement on what is to happen next, then follow-up appropriately.

Points to Remember

- Quality service professionals train themselves to take people seriously in every service contact.

- Questions help you clarify issues and can also help ensure that you are giving the most complete service possible.

- Telephone communications make contact faster and easier, yet can hamper the quality of the customer connection.

- Volume, speed and tone must be controlled so they remain positive factors.

- The lack of visual cues makes voice enhancement necessary to create a good impression.

- In responding to telephone cues you must check for understanding as well as move the discussion forward.

Exercise 11: Effective Telephone Communication

Question 1) Why is it more difficult to give customers your full attention over the phone than it is in person?

Question 2) When you're the customer over the phone, what can you do to assure that the person serving *you* gives *you* her full attention?

Question 3) Does your work area have any specific phone standards as to how people are supposed to greet callers and identify themselves, their area, and/or the institution?

Question 4) From your work here, what's your sense of how other offices on campus greet callers and identify themselves?

Question 5) How can you tell when a caller is confused?

Question 6) Why is it much more difficult to read customers over the phone than in person? What can you do to overcome this difficulty?

Exercise 12: Practice in Interpreting Telephone Cues

Cue	Your Interpretation	Your Response
Total silence after you've explained a procedure to a student.		
"I have to do *what?*" asks a parent.		
"You're kidding!" in a sing-song tone.		
"You're kidding!" in a sarcastic tone.		
"Two days isn't very much time," from a co-worker.		
Computer keys clicking during the conversation.		
"Uh...oh, sorry. What did you say?"		
"Then who *does* know?"		
"I've been on hold for 5 minutes already."		

SECTION 4: Advanced Skills in Transferring and Screening Calls

"Could you hold?" No one likes to hear that he is being put on hold or being transferred. Being on hold or transferred means waiting and probably having to explain your problem all over again to someone new. Holds and transfers are, however, a normal part of telephone communication. Sometimes it seems you spend half your day transferring calls from one department to another. How can you limit your holds and transfers or at least make them less of a nuisance for your customers? What part do telephone skills play in building a service culture? That's what you will look at in this section.

Faculty and staff need to transfer calls to other offices on campus from time to time. For faculty, this may only happen a few times a week, while a staff member in one of the academic offices may handle dozens of transfers every day. Regardless of how frequently you transfer calls, it's important to remember that every *single* transfer creates a powerful impression on the customer.

Top Ten Most Irritating Transfer Situations

The transfer can either be handled smoothly, cleanly and quickly, or it can be mishandled in any number of ways. Think back to the last time *you* were transferred into a black hole and you've got the idea. Here are some of the transfer situations that irritate customers most.

1. You're transferred to one or more wrong offices.

2. You're transferred before you have a chance to fully explain what you want.

3. You have to explain your situation or question over and over again to different people.

4. You're transferred without knowing to what office or person you're being transferred.

5. You aren't given a transfer number to call back if you're disconnected.

6. You're kept on hold an excessive time before the transfer.

7. You're transferred back to someone you've already talked to.

8. You're disconnected in the middle of the transfer.

9. You're transferred to a number that is busy, or there is no answer.

10. The person handling your call isn't familiar with campus phone technology.

You'll know you're doing a great job of transferring calls when you eliminate these irritating situations for your customers.

Why Callers Need to Be Transferred

Sometimes callers must be transferred because they've called the wrong number, or the person they've asked for works in a different area, or they have additional business with another department. Callers expect to be transferred in these situations, and you can make these transfers quickly and positively by using your best transfer skills.

Other times, though, callers might not feel as positively about being transferred. Perhaps they've called the right department, but you can't answer their question. Maybe the only person who can help them is gone for the day. Maybe your systems are set up so that seemingly related questions must be handled by different departments.

It's understandable why situations such as these might try the customer's patience. That's why it's even more important to project a professional, efficient image during the call transfer. Listening, giving the customer your name and keeping the customer informed about what is going on can help turn the most problematic telephone transfer into a positive experience.

A call transfer is positive when:

- You sound pleased to connect the caller.
- You listen carefully and fully understand the caller's needs.
- You complete the transfer quickly.
- You transfer the caller correctly.
- You only transfer the call when necessary.

Remember that colleges and universities are very open and accessible. Businesses of comparable size handle most incoming calls through a customer service office. This approach makes it easier to control quality because fewer people need to be trained, up-to-date information is more readily at hand and fewer calls need to be transferred. Transferring calls effectively within a college or university is truly an advanced skill.

Steps to a Professional Call Transfer

Call transfers are perfect breeding grounds for the campus run-around. Be prepared. Know which department handles what, and know the best people to call for answers. If a call transfer is necessary, follow these steps:

1. Check staff availability

Let the caller know you will be placing them on hold while you check to see if someone is available to assist them. During this step, you may say: "I'll check to see if Robert is in. Can you hold for a moment?"

For calls to other departments, your phone system may or may not allow you to check staff availability in another

office. If this is the case, be sure to tell the caller where the call is being transferred and the number.

2. Give caller an update and offer to relay information

When you know a staff member is available, return to your caller and tell her so. You may also want to give the caller the co-worker's phone number, in case she needs to call again. You might say: "Robert is in and I can transfer you now. In case you need to call him again, his number is 555-3395. Would you like me to tell him who's calling?"

Notice that the offer to relay the caller's name is phrased in such a way as to sound like a benefit to the customer, when actually it can be a help to your co-worker. This phrasing, though, sounds much more customer-focused than "Who's calling, please?"

3. Contact staff member and announce call

Now put your caller on hold once more, ring your co-worker's extension, and announce the caller. You might say: "Hi, Robert, it's Carol in admissions. I'm transferring Sue Keller to you—she needs some help applying for a loan. Here she is." Then make the transfer. Give your co-worker as much information as you can about the caller and his or her needs—this will help your team member prepare for the call.

This simple three-step process avoids unpleasant surprises for customers and staff. Smooth and professional call transfers make customer service over the telephone more pleasant for everyone.

Are You In or Out?

Screening calls can be a tricky business. Although many people associate call screening with avoiding a call, sometimes calls are screened in order to identify an extremely important caller and get them through quickly.

Perfecting your screening techniques allows you to help your customers better by identifying them and discovering their reason for calling. Advanced telephone screening techniques can improve your questioning skills, allowing you to assess customer problems more quickly.

Here is one reason screening calls is such a challenge: many students and parents call and ask for a specific person if they have a question or problem. Prospective and admitted students may receive personal letters from many different people on a campus, including the president, academic department heads, as well as directors of advising, admissions, orientation and financial aid. With today's sophisticated word processing technologies, these form letters can seem very personalized.

Consider the situation of an admissions office. Imagine that you are a prospective student who has applied for admission and is waiting for a decision. After you applied, you received a letter from the admissions office acknowledging the receipt of your application. The letter, signed by the director of admissions, Robert Hamilton, closes with the statement, "Please don't hesitate to call if you have any questions."

Students and their parents *will* call with questions, and a certain percentage of callers will ask to talk with the person from whom they received a letter. The problem in the example above is that the director of admissions may not take any routine calls from prospective students. But the problem is even more complicated. When the caller says, "I'd like to speak with Robert Hamilton," the call could be from anybody: a rejected applicant, a high school counselor, the dean of the law school, Mr. Hamilton's brother, or the mechanic working on his car. Some of these people Mr. Hamilton will want to speak with, others he will not. This situation demands advanced skills from any staff who might handle the call. In fact, everybody involved has some responsibilities in this situation—including Mr. Hamilton.

The role of staff in screening calls. For staff, the primary responsibility is effectively screening calls without making the callers feel devalued. To effectively screen calls you need to find out something about the caller and about the nature of the call. However, you want to be very careful how you solicit this information. If you say to a caller, "May I have your name, please?" the caller will likely get the impression that Mr. Hamilton might be available for some people but not others. A better question is, "Would you like me to tell him who is calling?" Likewise, to determine the nature of the call, don't say, "May I ask what the call is concerning?" Instead, say something like, "Will he know what the call is concerning?"

The role of administrators and faculty in screening calls. Administrators have a responsibility to work with staff and student employees to develop screening procedures that work. As an administrator you can help staff in some of the following ways. Alert your staff if you are expecting an important call—especially from someone whose name may not be familiar to staff answering the phone. If you have a private line in addition to a general office number, you may want staff to screen calls differently on the private line. If you're not taking any calls, tell staff who the exceptions are—a spouse or child, a physician, etc. If you're in a meeting, tell staff the names of any callers for whom you could be interrupted.

Transferring and screening calls opens the way for you to find out more about your customers and gives you a unique opportunity to help them. Finding out about your customers helps you build on your commitment to quality by fine-tuning your questioning skills.

Points to Remember

- Every phone transfer creates a powerful impression on the customer.

- Multiple phone transfers are exasperating for customers and staff.

- A professional transfer includes: checking for availability, giving an update, announcing the call and making the transfer.

- Everyone on campus—faculty, administrators, staff and student employees—needs to transfer calls effectively.

- Effective call screening requires a partnership between staff and administrators.

- Advanced call screening techniques allow you to better serve customers and co-workers.

Exercise 13: Advanced Transfer and Screening Techniques

Question 1) Could you spot what was missing from that last transfer? Could the staff member have done something more when Dr. Polanski wasn't available?

Question 2) In the first example Jan said, "Would you like me to tell him who's calling?" How does this give a different impression than "Who's calling, please?"

Question 3) Service providers often ask callers the routine question, "May I ask what the call is concerning?" What is a better question to ask, and why?

Question 4) What are some common challenges you have in screening calls?

Question 5) What screening techniques do you use now that you find work well?

Question 6) Do any of your offices have specific policies or procedures in place for screening calls?

SECTION 5: Meeting Individual and Campuswide Phone Challenges

Advanced Connections focuses on relationships, on how staff, administrators and faculty work together to build a service culture. Nowhere is the need to work together more important than in meeting daily phone challenges such as taking messages effectively and reducing needless phone transfers.

Effective Message-taking

How many times has this happened to you? You find a message on your desk that says, "Please call Joan at 634-9489." You have no idea who this person is, why she is calling, or when she might be available. Perhaps the caller doesn't need to talk to you at all, but needs information from someone else. Incomplete messages like this lead to delays, frustration and poor service.

You can avoid situations like this by applying the best communication skills you've learned so far in the program—listen carefully, ask the right questions and take each caller seriously. In this section you will learn about effective ways to take and leave messages, as well as how to reduce phone run-around.

Handling phone messages well is an advanced skill. Call-backs take time. Before you take a message, make an effort to find out if someone else can help the caller: "May I take a message or could someone else help you?" Often someone else can help. As a result, you've served the caller quickly and efficiently, and avoided needless call-backs.

If you do need to take a message, be sure you *take* enough information to make the call-back as productive as possible and *give* enough information to the caller so they know what to expect.

Information to take from callers

When caller is requesting a return contact:

- Name
- Phone number
- Fax number or e-mail address
- Two or three specific times or blocks of time caller will be available
- Purpose of call

When caller is requesting information:

- Name
- Phone number
- Fax number or e-mail address
- Complete mailing address
- Specific information requested

Information to give to callers

- Your name
- Any alternate numbers they could use to reach the person they're calling
- Any appropriate information concerning when the caller might or might not expect to receive a return contact. For instance, "Mr. Hamilton is unavailable for the next four days and won't be able to return your call until after Wednesday."

Follow these simple steps each time you offer to take a message for another team member:

1. Leave caller on hold for no more than 30 seconds.
2. Offer to find someone else to help when the staff member is not available.

3. Determine the action step, that is, what needs to be done. Not every message will necessitate a call-back. Some messages are requests for information, others simply pass on information.

4. Get all the information you need, depending on the action step.

5. Read back the message to verify accuracy, checking spelling as needed.

6. Thank the caller.

7. Add date, time of call and your name.

8. Deliver the message immediately to the co-worker's desk, mail slot, e-mail, or other location set aside for messages.

If your campus uses voice mail, give callers an option of how they wish to leave a message: "Would you like me to direct you to their voice mail or leave a message with me?" The voice mail option will save you time, but you also may sacrifice some quality control. When you take a message properly, you're in control. You can be sure to write down complete information about the caller, how and when they can be reached, and what the call is concerning. In other words, you'll get all the information you need because you know the right questions to ask.

When you transfer a call to someone's voice mail, you lose some of that control and the result may be incomplete messages. To avoid this, remind callers to leave a complete message, including how and when they can be reached. This subject will be covered more thoroughly in Section 6: Managing Voice Mail Effectively.

Effective Message-leaving

As the old saying goes, "Drive defensively." You may be a good driver yourself, but you still need to watch out for other drivers. Similar advice applies when it comes to leaving messages. You may have excellent message-taking skills, but the people who take your messages may not.

Don't settle for shoddy service. If the person taking your message doesn't ask you the right questions, then step forward yourself with statements such as:

1. "I'll be out this afternoon, but I can be reached between 10 and 4 tomorrow."

2. "If he calls when I am not available, ask him to leave two times when I could reach him."

3. "Would you please read my name, number and message back to me?"

Cutting Back on Call Transfers

In the first session you saw how the campus run-around affects people when communicating face to face. The run-around is even more common—and maddening—when it happens over the phone.

No campus can build a first-class service culture without first reducing the number of needless phone transfers. And that's everyone's responsibility. It takes teamwork to make a phone system work efficiently for both callers and staff. It takes your involvement.

Your commitment to teamwork can help you cut down on transfers. Instead of transferring a caller to one of your team members and forcing the caller to repeat him or herself, you can call your co-worker and get the information yourself. Your knowledge of the way your office works helps you get the information quickly for your caller. Keeping up good relationships with your team members makes you more effective.

Multiple phone transfers usually start when callers don't know who best can help them. That's where your skill and persistence pay off.

You need information to transfer calls correctly. You need to know exactly what the caller wants, and you need to know who in your institution can provide it.

The role of staff in reducing call transfers

- Reduce mistakes. If you have to transfer a call, make sure it's to the correct office.

- Resist quick transfers. Really listen to what the caller needs before quickly transferring a call to another office.

- Know your institution. Take time to learn how your institution works so that you can help callers determine who best can help them.

- Help to identify transfer problems. Pay attention to where you generally transfer calls and where you get incoming transfers from. These patterns may indicate communication problems that need to be addressed.

- Freely share information within your office and with other offices. For instance, if your office is involved with a large or special event on campus for which you expect many calls, make sure other offices know what's happening and how they can help.

- Keep control of the call. If the caller and you are unsure to whom the call should be transferred, put the caller on hold and make the call yourself.

The role of administrators in reducing call transfers

- Provide orientation and ongoing training in key phone skills such as call transfers.

- Set clear service standards and expectations for how staff are to handle calls.

- Work with administrators in other offices to identify call transfer patterns and to reduce unnecessary transfers.

- Communicate information to other offices to help them better serve callers without immediately transferring calls.

- Develop point-of-contact guides for staff to use to provide routine information to callers.

Throughout Advanced Connections you've learned about the importance of preventing problems. In the long-term, it is much better to reduce or prevent problems such as excessive transfers than it is to handle problems effectively *after* they arise.

Fact-Finding Questions That Boost Service Delivery

Every customer has a unique set of expectations, and every situation adds a new dimension. Ask fact-finding questions that will uncover customer expectations and steer you toward a successful service experience. Here are some examples:

- "How may I help you?"

- "Are you familiar with how this process/procedure/ form works?"

- "Would you prefer to hold for a couple of minutes, or should I take your number and call you back?"

- "When do you need this information?"

- "Would getting this information by express mail be worth the extra cost for you?"

- "Is a verbal approval okay, or do you need a signed document sent to you?"

- "Since she's not in, can someone else help you?"

- "Would you like me to find someone else who can help you?" (If yes, then: "What exactly did you need from _____?")

Add fact-finding questions specific to your department and your customers' needs.

Points to Remember

- Call transfers can be a positive experience when handled smoothly and professionally.

- Fact-finding questions help to uncover needs and prevent needless transfers.

- Messages taken for others must be detailed and thorough, as well as delivered promptly.

- Everyone can play a role in reducing needless phone transfers.

- Effective message-leaving is as important as effective message-taking.

Exercise 14: Handling Difficult Transfer Situations

Question 1) When someone is unavailable, what helpful questions could you ask the caller?

Question 2) What do you do if there's no one available immediately to help the customer?

Question 3) How important is it to always help the person as much as possible right away?

Question 4) What can we do to reduce the number of transfers? What would the effect of this be on the customer?

Question 5) What kind of training and information do you think you'd need to help you reduce the number of phone transfers?

Follow-Up Departmental Activity: Reducing Call Transfers

1. What are the main offices that transfer calls to your office?

2. What are the main offices you transfer calls to?

3. What are examples of common calls mistakenly sent to your area?

Ideas for Reducing Phone Transfers

Idea 1: _____

Action steps needed: _____

_____

_____

Idea 2: _____

Action steps needed: _____

_____

_____

Idea 3: _____

Action steps needed: _____

_____

_____

Optional Role-Play Exercise

This role-play provides an opportunity for you to practice your:

- Voice speed and volume
- Customer focus and degree of helpfulness
- Use of fact-finding questions
- Telephone transfer skills
- Message-taking skills

Scenarios:

1. A student calls a professor to ask when the last test will be graded. A department assistant answers the call, and finds the professor is not in.

2. A staff member in the bursar's office calls the library to see if they have any record of late fees being paid by a student. The person who knows how to look up that data is out for lunch.

3. The student president of the Math Club calls the bookstore to see if their screen-printed sweatshirts have arrived. The person who answers the phone just came on duty and doesn't know.

SECTION 6: Managing Voice Mail Effectively

Communication technologies such as voice mail and e-mail have many advantages. They allow you to:

- Leave longer and more detailed messages.

- Be assured that your message goes directly to the receiving party.

- Send and receive messages when offices are closed and to work from remote locations.

- Ensure greater accuracy by removing the "middle-person."

- Minimize telephone tag.

- Be more productive, by working with people and moving projects forward without face-to-face meetings.

- Improve the frequency of day-to-day communication and facilitate the flow of accurate, up-to-date information.

With these important advantages come a few disadvantages as well. These technologies:

- Can lead to incomplete and useless messages when used incorrectly by callers.

- Can lead to service breakdowns when messages aren't retrieved and acted upon promptly.

- Can lead to frustrating call-backs when voice mail systems don't allow users options to connect to live operators.

- Can lead to poor service because callers can't rely on the knowledge of human service providers to get them the help they need.

- Can project to callers an impersonal impression of your institution.

- Can threaten privacy when communications can be heard or seen by others.

The challenge is to use available technologies to their best advantage, while working to minimize the disadvantages.

Mastering Voice Mail

In the last section, you learned some effective ways to take and leave messages. That's a big enough challenge when two people are talking "live" on the phone. It's an even greater challenge with voice mail. The key to voice mail is to be just as good a message leaver as you are a message taker. Use the following suggestions to make the most out of your electronic communications.

Preserve the Personal Touch

A big part of customer service is the sense of unity or "family" you create for a customer. Look for ways to add the personal touch to your message—refer to a previous message, ask how the customer is, use humor, and so on.

Add Detail to Your Content

Add detail to your messages to compensate for the lack of visual cues, to prevent misunderstandings and to minimize the need for follow-up.

Use Effective Voice Mail Greetings

Use effective personal greetings for the three main types of messages: 1) greeting for no answer, 2) greeting for busy, and 3) special greetings for unusual circumstances such as when you are away from campus for extended periods.

This is especially important for faculty who may be away from campus for weeks or months at a time.

Change Your Personal Greetings Frequently

To help both you and your callers, change your personal greetings as often as you need to. Keep two important goals in mind: 1) to serve the people who call you, and 2) to reduce or eliminate the necessity for you to return calls. Here are some simple suggestions to help you reduce your number of call-backs:

1. Be aware of your audience. If people are likely to call you for information, especially about something of topical interest, look for ways to help them in your greeting: "If you're calling to set up an advising time, there's a sign-up sheet on my door"; or "If you're calling to receive a copy of the new enrollment projections, please dial 453 and ask for Dave"; or "If you're calling about the article in today's student newspaper about graduation analyses, the deadline is March 9th, not March 1st as was printed in the paper."

2. If you plan to be away from your office for more than a day, don't leave an unqualified message such as, "I am unavailable to take your call at this time. Please leave your name, your telephone number and a brief message and I will return your call as soon as possible." Instead, include information in the message that fixes time and duration, "I am out of the office until October 18th. Please leave your name...."

Give Your Callers an Out

Never leave your callers hanging in "voice mail jail." Always provide information about how to access a live person if needed. This can be as simple as, "For immediate assistance, please press 1 to return to the department secretary."

Protect Privacy

Respect the customer's right to confidentiality and consider the consequences of any message being received by people other than the intended receiver. Position your computer screen so data and messages are not immediately readable by passersby. Keep your passwords to yourself. If you use an answering machine, listen to your messages at a low volume or when others are out of the area.

Build in a Plan for Follow-Up

Because you're not communicating face-to-face, make sure there's a way to know if your message got through.

Policies and Procedures for Managing Voice Mail

Avoid Using Automated Voice Systems to Answer Main Numbers

Voice mail is *not* designed to replace switchboard operators, receptionists or other front-line resources. Students, parents and other customers often don't know exactly who can best help them. Voice mail works best as a medium for leaving messages with *people* who are unavailable. *Offices* should never be "unavailable" during business hours.

Provide All Voice Mail Users With Sample Language to Use in Personal Greetings

Provide all users with sample language to use in personal greetings for the three main types of messages: 1) greeting for no answer, 2) greeting for busy, and 3) special greetings for unusual circumstances such as extended vacations.

Set Standards and Policies for Voice Mail Use

These standards and policies include:

1. How frequently people should check voice mail messages.

2. How frequently and under what circumstances people should change their voice mail greeting.

3. What options callers have for reaching a live person if needed.

Monitor How Voice Technologies Are Used on Your Campus

1. Know how many offices and individuals use voice mail.

2. Review copies of guidelines, policies and training/education materials used by departments.

3. Randomly check voice mail greetings used by individuals and offices on campus.

Points to Remember

- Communications technologies must be used carefully to derive full benefit from them.

- Detailed phone messages prevent the time-consuming game of telephone tag.

- Change voice mail greetings frequently.

- Communications are most effective when they remain personal, complete and private.

- Campuses need guidelines and policies to effectively manage voice mail.

Exercise 15: Handling Voice Mail Effectively

Question 1) In the last video segment, what caused the game of phone tag in the first example?

Question 2) What was the secret to Tom's success the second time around?

Question 3) How can you make use of these same techniques when you're leaving messages with a "live person" on the phone?

Question 4) Do the switchboard or any departments or offices on your campus use voice response (commonly called an automated attendant) to answer incoming calls and route them? If so, what impression is this likely to give customers?

Question 5) What other kinds of problems do customers typically have with voice mail?

Question 6) At your institution are there any standards, guidelines or policies for how voice mail is to be used by offices and individuals?

Question 7) If there are no standards, guidelines or policies, what kind would you like to see?

SECTION 7: Checking for Customer Satisfaction

In the first session you learned that there are five steps in the quality service process:

1. Discover customer requirements.

2. Develop service standards that promote excellence.

3. Design strategies that work.

4. Deliver quality service through every contact.

5. Check for satisfaction.

Checking for satisfaction both completes and begins the quality service process. It concludes a given service contact while also giving you more information about customer requirements, the first step in the model.

"Great work!" "Good job!" "Way to go!" You like to be appreciated for the work that you do. It makes you feel valuable, important and just plain good. In a quality service culture, you don't need to depend on a co-worker to know you are doing a good job; you can find out yourself from your customers.

When you eat at a nice restaurant, the waiter usually stops by your table after your food has arrived and asks how everything is. This procedure has become so customary that you come to depend on it. For instance, you may not ask for more water when the food is brought, because you know someone will be by later. How do you feel if someone doesn't come by? The food may be great and the atmosphere perfect, but if the staff doesn't bother to check for your satisfaction, you may feel their service is poor.

In this way, checking for satisfaction helps both the service provider and the customer. The service provider feels satisfaction when the customer is satisfied. Customers reinforce their own satisfaction when they respond, "Yes, everything was fine."

When Customers Aren't Satisfied

Sometimes when you check for satisfaction, you will learn that the customer is not satisfied. Discovering that a customer is not satisfied is an invitation to learn more about that particular customer and his or her requirements and to improve your service for others.

Here is an example. You notice a nontraditional student standing alone in your office. You approach him and check for satisfaction. "Is there anything I can help you with?" The student replies "no" but then tells you he has been waiting for half an hour for an answer to a question he posed to one of your co-workers. Quickly you get the information and discover what happened. Your co-worker handed the student off to another team member and left for lunch. Miscommunication caused a problem that you were able to fix by checking for satisfaction. In this case, checking for satisfaction revealed a breakdown in your system and allowed you to correct it.

Checking for Satisfaction Promotes Service Excellence

A customer is satisfied when the service received meets customer requirements—when, in the customer's estimation, he or she has received "quality" service.

Quality may mean different things to different customers, because it's all based on the customer's expectations. One customer expects quick service and gets quick service. In his mind, the service met his standards—his expectations —so he's satisfied. Another customer expects friendly service and gets quick service. In her mind, the service did not live up to her standards for quality—her expectations—so she's dissatisfied.

When customers are mentally measuring quality, they're deciding if they received:

1. *What* they wanted
2. *How* they wanted it
3. *When* they wanted it

For example, a customer may want—

- An answer to a question—the "what."

- The answer delivered in a courteous way—the "how."

- The answer given immediately, or at least within a few minutes—the "when."

You can see how these three components open the door for literally hundreds of combinations of customer expectations! That's why it's so critically important to check for customer satisfaction during every contact.

Customer Reactions

Customers typically react in these ways:

- When you meet expectations, check for satisfaction and get a "yes," the customer is pleased.

- When you do not meet expectations, then check for satisfaction and get a "no," the customer is concerned but hopeful that all will work out in the end.

- When you do not meet expectations and do not check for satisfaction, the customer is unhappy and you will pay the consequences now or later.

Customer "payback" can come in the form of angry words, negative word-of-mouth to friends or lost student recruitment. Isn't it better to check to ensure happy students and other customers?

How You Can Check for Satisfaction

Follow these guidelines for checking customer satisfaction:

- In every contact, check for satisfaction at least once.

- Demonstrate sincerity. Remember, students and other customers are the reason you're here, and quality service is your first priority.

- Use positive words and gestures. Never let the customer feel as if you've been inconvenienced—instead, make sure the customer knows you're eager to do more.

- View expressions of dissatisfaction with gratitude. The customer has just given you the gift of a second chance to do it right.

- Apologize for problems on behalf of your team.

- Fact-find for customer needs to determine the needs which are still unmet, then provide or arrange for the necessary service.

- End the contact with agreement—either agreement that the customer is satisfied or, as a last resort, agreement that there's nothing else you can do to help.

Points to Remember

- A customer is satisfied when the service received meets his or her expectations.

- Checking for satisfaction begins with fact-finding for needs.

- Satisfaction must be checked on every contact.

- There are steps that individuals, offices and departments can take to check for satisfaction.

- Expressions of dissatisfaction must be greeted graciously, then followed up with problem-solving efforts.

Exercise 16: Checking for Satisfaction

Question 1) As a staff or faculty member, what are some examples of ways in which you check for customer satisfaction?

Question 2) Listed below are ways in which departments or offices can check for satisfaction. What examples can you offer of ways your offices use one or more of these approaches right now?

- Informal written questionnaires and comment pieces
- More formal, standardized assessments of student satisfaction
- Monitoring the use of an office or service by customers
- Monitoring complaints

Question 3) Listed below are ways in which institutions can check for satisfaction. What examples can you offer of ways your institution uses one or more of these approaches right now?

- Focus groups with students or other customers
- Monitoring enrollment and retention rates
- More formal, standardized assessments of student satisfaction
- Monitoring the use of offices or services by customers
- Monitoring complaints

Question 4) What other approaches could you as an institution use to check for satisfaction?

Optional Role-Play Exercise: Checking for Satisfaction

Directions: Choose one or more of the following five scenarios as the subject for a role-play on checking for satisfaction. Each scenario is designed for one service provider and one customer. The Role-Play Observation Checklist is provided for observers to note comments about the role-plays.

For each of the scenarios, assume that—

- The service provider is expected to respond to the customer's request, then check for satisfaction.

- The customer will decide whether or not he or she is satisfied and tell the service provider.

- The service provider must respond appropriately, making sure that the customer is satisfied before closing the contact.

Scenario 1: A visiting professor stops a member of the security staff to ask for directions to a particular classroom building.

Scenario 2: A freshman asks his residence hall assistant for advice on a noisy roommate.

Scenario 3: A student cafeteria worker asks his supervisor about his paycheck that reflects an underpayment of five hours.

Scenario 4: A neighborhood homeowner complains to an administrator about students walking on her lawn every day.

Scenario 5: A caller asks to speak with the assistant dean, who is away at a convention for the week.

Questions for Role-Play Participants

Question 1) How successful were you in following all the guidelines to check for satisfaction?

Question 2) When you played the role of the customer, how did it feel when the service provider checked for satisfaction?

Role-Play Observation Checklist

Did _____, the service provider,
　　　　(name)

	Yes	No
Check for satisfaction?	☐	☐
Demonstrate sincerity?	☐	☐
Use positive words and gestures?	☐	☐
Greet dissatisfaction graciously?	☐	☐
Apologize for problems?	☐	☐
Fact-find for needs?	☐	☐
End with agreement?	☐	☐

I particularly liked the way this service provider: _____

_____

_____

A possible area for improvement: _____

_____

_____

My Commitment to Self-Development

As a result of what I've learned today, I am making a commitment to work toward improvement in these areas:

1. _____
2. _____
3. _____
4. _____
5. _____
6. _____
7. _____

I will ask _____ to help me check my
          (Co-worker's name)

progress on _____.
         (Date)

SESSION THREE: Meeting Service Challenges _____

SECTION 1: Introduction

In Session Three you will learn and practice a variety of skills to meet service challenges, such as restoring customer satisfaction after problems occur.

In the first two sessions you discussed and practiced the skills you need to deliver quality service. In this session you will explore the resources, options and alternatives to help you solve service problems and restore customer satisfaction. Service recovery skills can be difficult to cultivate, but building your skills in this area will help you maintain positive relationships with both your internal and external customers.

Service recovery is important, but remember that by far the best long-term approach is to prevent problems before they occur.

Session Three Topics

Identifying moments of truth and their impact on customer satisfaction. Every experience a customer has with your college or university is made up of countless face-to-face contacts, or "moments of truth." It is from these moments that customers form their opinions about the way they were treated. In this session, you will learn how to recognize these individual moments and use them to help your customers and improve your campus service image.

Mastering the steps to service recovery. Turning a customer's dissatisfaction into satisfaction is at the heart of this section. You may know more than you think about smoothing over a difficult situation. The skills and pointers in this section will enhance your knowledge and build your confidence.

Uncovering and solving system-related problems. Often it is your institution's policy, not you, that the customer is dissatisfied with. Recognizing system-related problems and providing effective solutions, even when your hands may seem tied, are explored in this section.

Knowing when to ask for help. When you work in service teams, it is natural to ask other team members for help. This section covers when and how to ask for help. It also covers the benefits of empowering staff to promote service excellence.

Educating customers through shared problem solving. Every service provider is a teacher. This section shows how you can educate your customers to be more knowledgeable and self-sufficient.

Developing quality service action plans. Developing set guidelines and procedures for service recovery can improve service, take the stress off front-line people, and make service more uniform. This special section is designed to initiate specific service recovery plans that can be adapted to fit your department or office.

Moments of Truth

There's a popular expression in our culture that you've probably heard many times. Maybe you've been helping your fifth-grader work on a science project about electricity. You've built an impressive-looking contraption, installed a crude generator, and now you're ready to create electricity. As you're about to flip the switch, you and your child look at each other and you say anxiously, "We've come to the moment of truth."

Or maybe you've been hiking in the woods when you come to a fork in the trail. You're not sure which path to take and you mutter to yourself, "Hmmm. Which one of these will take me back? Looks like a moment of truth."

Over the years, you've come to understand from experiences like these that a "moment of truth" is a crucial time. It's the crowning moment that brings to fruition everything that came before—or the big event that will change everything that comes afterward.

Moments of Truth in Quality Service

When it comes to serving customers, *every* moment of the customer's experience is a big event. That's because every moment creates an impression in the customer's mind of you and your institution.

A moment of truth, then, is any impression-creating contact between the customer and the organization. The impression gained can be either positive, negative, or something in between.

Sometimes a customer's impressions are gained when you're nowhere in sight—perhaps a parent is reading an alumni bulletin and is impressed with what's happening on campus. That's a positive moment of truth. Other times, you have a direct impact on the impression your customer is getting—because the impression is based on what you're saying and doing. Is the impression you're creating positive or negative?

Every customer experience contains many moments of truth—many quick impressions that register in the mind of your customer. This simple fact has tremendous implications for you.

No matter what task you're working on, you're always serving either an external or internal customer. You're creating an endless number of moments of truth. So you must be "on your toes" during every second of every work day. Everything you do and say must be done as well as you can. The result will be positive moments of truth and customer satisfaction.

What's the Big Deal?

So *what* if customers experience a negative moment of truth now and then? They'll get over it, right?

Perhaps not. A mother of five was so disheartened by a summer camp's lack of accommodation for her physically challenged son that she canceled the reservations for all five of her children. A longtime contributor to a university's annual fund vowed never to give another dime when a harried staff member suggested he call back another time because she was "too busy" to help him.

What may seem like "no big deal" to a service provider is often a *very* big deal to students and other customers.

On the other hand, there are also countless examples of students and alumni who have become your institution's strongest advocates because the little things—the individual moments of truth—were handled correctly and professionally.

Positive moments of truth are powerful motivators for your customers. They inspire your customers to take the next step—and whether that step is toward you or away from you depends on the quality of the moment.

It has been said that customers have three characteristics: 1) they have needs, 2) they have options, and 3) they have portable loyalties. For students—the most numerous and most important customers for colleges and universities— these three characteristics translate into the following: 1) the need is to receive a quality education, 2) the option is to choose one school over many others in the recruitment process, and 3) students are willing to transfer from one school to another if they feel their needs aren't being met.

Student recruitment and student retention are the lifeblood of most colleges and universities, both public and private. The thousands of moments of truth that happen on your campus every day all add up to an overall quality of life that will determine the success of your institution's recruitment and retention.

The Impact of Mishandled Moments of Truth

When you mishandle a moment of truth—in other words, allow the customer to gain a negative impression of you or your institution—the effects are felt far and wide.

- As many as 95% of your unhappy students and other customers will not tell you they're unhappy, so you have no opportunity to fix their problem. They'll simply walk away or hang up the phone and remain unhappy with your institution. This means that for every complaint you hear, there are 20 you haven't heard.

- Each unhappy customer *will* tell an average of 10—and sometimes as many as 20—other people about his or her displeasure. And bad news travels fast.

- Unhappy students can affect your efforts to recruit other students. Because recommendations from acquaintances carry twice the impact of paid advertising, your recruiting messages may not be believed by those you'd like to convince.

- Non-complainers are less likely to return for additional service than those who complain. They'll simply look for other ways to get their needs met, and you'll never know why you never see them again.

Points to Remember

- A moment of truth is an opportunity for students and other customers to gain an impression of you and your institution.

- Negative moments of truth can outweigh many positive moments that came before.

- Mishandled moments of truth—when not overcome—create dissatisfied customers who share their experience with others.

- Mishandled moments of truth that are eventually overcome with quality service create highly loyal customers.

- Quality service relationships with both internal and external customers are built upon positive moments of truth.

Exercise 17: An Introduction to Service Recovery

Question 1) Who has a story to share about service recovery when you were the customer of some business or organization other than our own institution?

Question 2) Who has a story to tell about excellent service recovery on your campus? Write below any examples you know of at your institution.

Question 3) What are the common elements in all of these examples? What did all the service providers do that made such a good impression on the customer? Let's list them.

Optional Exercise: Analyzing Moments of Truth

Moments of truth for my *internal* customers: _____

_____

_____

_____

Moments of truth for my *external* customers: _____

_____

_____

_____

SECTION 2: Service Recovery

It's clear that a bungled moment of truth creates a negative impression on students and other customers, and that unhappy students cause problems for any college or university.

The key is to actively uncover as many problems as you can—don't let your customers remain silently unhappy—then work hard to solve any problems you find. That's where service recovery comes in.

Service recovery is the positive, proactive steps taken to undo damage created when a customer perceives a problem. It means turning the customer's dissatisfaction into satisfaction—transforming a negative impression into a positive one.

It doesn't matter the type of problem, its severity, who's to blame, or even if there really is a problem at all—if the customer has become unhappy with the service or your institution, it's time for service recovery. Think of it this way: problems make customers feel bad; service recovery helps them feel good again.

You already know a lot more about service recovery than you might think—you've experienced it many times before, both in your personal life and your work life. Think of some examples of moments of truth in your department or office: when you answer the phone, greet a customer at the door, ask a co-worker for assistance in front of a customer, etc. How do you think these moments of truth are perceived by your customers? Are they impressed with your friendliness? Do they respond to your smile? Do they think the people in your department communicate and work well together? When the answer to these questions is a resounding "Yes!" then you know your service is excellent. If you are unsure or feel that a moment of truth has resulted in a negative experience for your customers, then service recovery is needed.

Customer Expectations of Recovery

Just as customers have expectations of the day-to-day service they will receive from you, they also have expectations of what will happen when something goes wrong. When problems occur, your customers generally expect you and your organization to:

1. Offer an apology for the inconvenience

While this seems simple enough, customers actually receive apologies less often than you'd think. Some service providers say they hesitate to apologize because they feel they've done nothing wrong.

Remember that an apology is not the same as taking blame. Instead, you're telling the customer you're sorry he or she has been inconvenienced.

2. Offer a "fair fix" for the problem

Customers rarely make outrageous demands. So what seems "fair" to them is often quite a bit less than you might think. Often a careful explanation and sincere effort to provide the right service the *second* time are all that are needed to satisfy the customer.

3. Treat the customer in a way that suggests care for the customer and concern for fixing the problem

Every service recovery experience is just that—an *experience*. The customer is interested in two things: the outcome, or the final resolution of the problem; and the process, how painful or painless it was to reach the final solution.

Service providers who grudgingly serve the customer, as if to snarl, "There. Are you happy now?" go through the motions but make the process so painful that the customer's negative impression takes a turn for the worse.

4. Offer some value-added atonement for the inconvenience

This is often referred to as "making amends." It's what a restaurant does when it offers a free dessert because the dinner arrived cold. It's what the dry cleaner does when it offers to deliver your cleaning that wasn't ready on time. And it's what the co-worker in admissions does when she offers to work through lunch to make corrections on the report you asked for.

Because you work in higher education, it's usually not possible to give the customer something extra at no charge (like the free dessert). But that's okay, because making amends often requires nothing more than a sincere effort to go the extra mile and make sure things progress smoothly from here on out.

Do you, as a customer, hold these same expectations for service recovery?

Now it's time for you to look at each of these steps a little more closely.

Five Steps to Service Recovery

There's a proven path that leads your customer from a negative impression to customer satisfaction. Five steps to take:

1. Acknowledge the problem

Make sure the customer knows you have heard and understood his or her concern.

2. Apologize

Say "I'm sorry" immediately to diffuse customer annoyance and demonstrate that you're on the same side.

3. Problem solve

Look for creative ways to remedy the problem, remembering that the goal is customer satisfaction, not staff convenience.

4. Communicate and make amends

Share your solution with the customer, gain agreement, and offer to "make it up" to the customer if possible.

5. Implement and follow up

Solve the problem, keep your promises, and check to be sure the customer is now satisfied.

What Problem?

The most important step to solving any problem is to first acknowledge that there is a problem. Agreeing that your customer does indeed have a problem shows that you understand and often changes the customer's attitude immediately.

A student has brought an overdue notice to your desk at the circulation department of the library. He is angry because he returned the book before it was due and this is the third notice he has received. "That's got to be frustrating," you say. "Do you remember when you returned it?" You acknowledge his problem and are empathic to how he must be feeling. Now you can get to work solving it.

Angry customers are expecting a fight. They assume they will be told, "You're wrong," or at least to be treated with suspicion. When you say, "You're right," or "I understand," they are caught off guard. Suddenly you are not the antagonist anymore, and they are usually more willing to work with you toward a solution. Acknowledging the problem is not only good service recovery, it can save you from a lot of abuse.

Saying "I'm Sorry"

Apologizing can sometimes be difficult. You may not feel that the situation was your fault or you don't want to accept blame for a problem you don't fully understand. Hearing an apology, though, is important for your customers. They want to know that someone is accepting some responsibility for their situation and helping them.

> **Five Steps to Service Recovery**
>
> 1. Acknowledge the problem.
> 2. Apologize.
> 3. Problem solve.
> 4. Communicate and make amends.
> 5. Implement and follow up.

An apology doesn't have to be the same as admitting you did wrong. It lets customers know you understand their problem and are on their side. "I'm sorry you've had to wait so long. That can't be easy when you don't feel well." Simple statements that express your regret can go a long way to turning a dissatisfied customer into a satisfied one.

Problem Solving

After you have acknowledged the problem and apologized for the confusion, you are ready to get down to finding an acceptable solution. Using the skills you've already talked about in the previous sessions will help you troubleshoot through a problem with your customer.

Look again at the library example. You have already acknowledged the problem and apologized for the inconvenience. Now you are ready to find a solution. Searching the records you find that the book isn't listed as being turned in. "I don't have the book listed as being checked in," you tell the student.

"I brought it back. I know I did," the student says.

"Well, I'll need to do some checking to find out what happened. It could have gotten misplaced. May I take your name and number and call you tomorrow and let you know what I find out?"

Letting customers know what is going on and keeping them informed of your process helps them understand that you are giving them all the help you can. Taking their name and promising to call them, to follow up, shows them you value their time and are sensitive to their needs. Even when you can't find a solution to a problem, keeping a customer informed and being sensitive will result in a positive impression.

Communicating Solutions and Making Amends

You've seen in previous sessions how delicate the lines of communication can be. Making yourself clear and helping your customers understand is paramount when you are telling them about the solution to their problem.

Spell everything out for your customer, from what happened to what is going to happen and what it all means in the end. Your customers are more likely to be satisfied with the service they receive, even if the outcome isn't what they wanted, if they understand all you went through to deliver that service.

The same is true for making amends. Explain completely to your customers what is involved and how they will benefit from the solution you are offering.

In the library example, you contacted the other departments in charge of checking in books and found nothing. Policy states that the student must be charged for the book. You call the student and explain all the steps you took to find the lost book. You then explain that if the book can't be found, the student must be charged the price of the book. Since he has come in and told his side of the story, you offer to wait until the end of the term before assessing any charges. Hopefully, the book will be found and returned. You promise to keep him informed if there are any changes in this situation.

Even though this wasn't the best of outcomes, you were able to make it clear to the student that you had done all you could and you would continue to work on a solution. He may not be pleased about being charged for the book, but he should be satisfied with the service he received. Making sure your customer is satisfied brings you to the next step in service recovery.

Implementation and Follow-Up

Your commitment to quality service is most rigorously tested over time. Implementing solutions for your customers and providing comprehensive follow-up is often what separates excellent service from mediocre service.

It is the end of the term, and the book your student claims he turned in still has not been checked in. You have no option but to charge him the price of the book. Instead of simply assessing a fine, you write the student a note reminding him of the situation and informing him of the fine. You explain that since he said he turned in the book, you have made a special arrangement with your department head. The student and the library will split the cost for the book. Your letter lets him know that the extra $20 on his student account is for his half of the book value.

Your service recovery in this example has been exemplary. You kept in good communication with the student, looked into his problem, found a fair solution, worked with your team members to implement that solution, and followed up with the student about the outcome.

It is easy to be concerned about customers' problems when they are right in front of you, but the real test comes when they leave. This is where most service recovery falls apart. Keeping up your commitment to your customers over time demonstrates your conscientiousness and can dramatically influence their view of your service. The student probably had forgotten all about the lost book. Your letter made him feel special. It was obvious that you cared about how he felt since you went to all the trouble to solve his problem and kept him informed. This is probably the best this student will ever feel about getting fined.

Service Recovery in Higher Education

Imagine, for a moment, that you work in an ice cream store. A man and his daughter enter the store and order two double-dip cones. The store is busy and you are slow in filling their order. You also misunderstand the order and give them the wrong ice cream. To make matters worse, you overcharge them and they correct you. Outside the store, the little girl drops her cone and spills her ice cream. With tearful daughter in tow, the man re-enters the store and asks to buy a new one. You give him another ice cream cone at no charge, offer a wet towel to clean his daughter's hands, and give his daughter a free T-shirt to help make up for her ruined dress.

In the ice cream store example, service recovery was easy. You had tangible items of value to give your customers to make up for their trouble. When you deal with retail or service businesses as a customer, you expect that they will be able to offer you a variety of options in service recovery situations. Grocery stores and clothing shops routinely take back or exchange products you aren't satisfied with. In cases of serious problems, you may expect discounts on future purchases, or free services related to what you are buying. In your college and university departments and offices, however, you may have very few options to make amends to people who are upset or dissatisfied.

For example, consider the following situations that concern institutional mistakes or problems that affect students negatively. For each situation, a substantive service recovery option is listed. Many institutions do not routinely take these kinds of recovery options to recover from service problems. Would your institution?

1. The institution makes a mistake on a student's degree audit that necessitates the student stay in school an extra term to graduate. *Service recovery option:* the institution gives the student a tuition break for the extra term.

2. A student is misadvised by his faculty advisor and takes the wrong class to satisfy a requirement. *Service recovery option:* the student receives a tuition refund to apply to the right class.

3. A new student is put in temporary housing in a residence hall lounge. *Service recovery option:* the student receives a discount on her residence hall charges or gets a higher priority for the next round of room selection.

4. A student comes to register at her scheduled time and waits in line two hours to register. By the time the student registers, two of the classes she needs are closed. *Service recovery option:* the student receives special preference on getting into the two closed classes.

Service recovery in these situations is challenging, but not impossible. The best approach, however, as you have seen throughout Advanced Connections, is to get it right the first time. That's why the focus of Session Three and all of Advanced Connections is on working together to prevent problems.

Points to Remember

- Successful service providers constantly search to uncover customer problems.

- Your first response to a customer's complaint must convey a positive, can-do attitude.

- Customers expect an apology and fair fix for their problems.

- Effective service recovery includes: acknowledging the problem, apologizing, problem solving, communicating and making amends, and implementing and following up.

Exercise 18: Reviewing the Basics of
Service Recovery

Question 1) In the last video example, the cold burger seemed to be the student's own fault. Why should we be concerned about service recovery in a case like this?

Question 2) How do you think the student would feel if you made it clear that he was to blame?

Question 3) Does this situation—when you feel the problem is the customer's fault—create any special challenges to you as a service provider?

Exercise 19: First Response

DIRECTIONS: When the customer has a problem, your first response to his or her complaint sets the stage for the rest of your encounter. Make sure your first response is a positive, customer-oriented one! Include both an apology and assurance that the problem will be solved. Rewrite the following response statements.

	Original First Reaction	More Effective First Response
To a parent whose son received an "F" for a class he didn't officially drop:	"Those are the rules."	
To a student charged a late fee:	"You shouldn't have waited so long to pay your bill!"	
To a supervisor questioning a delivery of material:	"I'm not the one who placed that order."	
To a co-worker returning your work for correction:	"I'm busy now."	
To a caller who asks when he can get a problem corrected:	"I don't know."	
To an alumnus irritated with slow response to a request:	"You must not know much about how a campus like this operates!"	

130

SECTION 3: Service Recovery When It's Your Fault

Nobody likes to be wrong. Being wrong sometimes means much more than a bruised ego; it can result in serious problems with your customers. Responding to service problems that are your fault is especially challenging and requires specific considerations.

Take Charge of a Recovery

Earlier in the program you talked about teams and about how teams are made up of leaders, not followers. Your leadership skills are especially important in service recovery. Excellent service providers don't just react to a problem, they take charge and lead a customer to a solution.

Show You Care

When customers take the time to point out an area of weakness, they are showing you they care enough to give you a second chance. It is important, therefore, for you to show your customers the same caring attitude.

You show you care about your customers in many ways. You use empathy statements to let people know you can see the situation from their point of view. You take responsibility and work efficiently to show your customers that you respect their time. You let customers know what is going on and include them in the problem-solving process. Each of these approaches is important in any service situation. In service recovery, showing you care is even more important. To perform a complete service recovery, you must pay special attention to customers in order to win them back.

Service Recovery Through Problem Solving

Occasionally you'll be called on to clean up a situation created by someone else. Remember that the responsibility for clean-up rests with the person who *discovers* the problem, not necessarily with the person who *created* the problem. The person in contact with the customer must take control and orchestrate a solution.

Keep the Customer in Focus

Avoid the tendency to blame or find fault with others. Instead, do whatever it takes to meet and exceed the customer's expectations. View a team member's mistake as an opportunity to learn a better way, rather than a reason to criticize or complain. Replace every "You shouldn't have done that!" with "How can we prevent this problem from happening again?"

Steps to Problem Solving

Whether you're confronted with a customer service problem or any other problem in your work or personal life, it's important to complete *all* the steps to problem solving. Faulty assumptions and incomplete information can steer you quickly in the wrong direction, causing your solution to be ineffective.

Here are the steps to problem solving. The steps are similar to the five steps of service recovery, except that the emphasis is on identifying and solving problems.

1. **Clarify the problem**

   When a customer complains, repeat back what you've heard. Feedback gives the customer a second chance to make the point clear. In addition, by restating a complaint, the customer may realize she has a different problem.

2. Fact-find for additional or hidden information

What is the real source of the problem? Look beyond the obvious symptoms to the underlying cause. Search for additional information — extenuating circumstances and background information—that will give you a clearer picture of what's really going on.

3. Generate possible solutions

Once you're clear on the real problem and what's causing it, think of all the possible ways to solve the problem. Caution: do *not* settle for the first solution that comes to mind! Better solutions often surface with a little more thought.

Remember that the statement "Our only choice is to..." is usually false! There is almost always more than one choice in any situation. Keep an open mind and find as many choices as you can.

4. Choose the best solution

Now you can start to get picky and throw out those solutions you don't like. Consider all your resources —people, time, budget, and customer preferences—to decide which solution will be most effective for all concerned. If two solutions seem appropriate for different reasons, put each to the test: which would best satisfy the customer?

5. Communicate and implement the solution

Tell the customer exactly what you plan to do, gain his or her agreement that this approach is satisfactory, then implement your solution.

> ### Problem-Solving Questions to Ask Yourself
>
> - What's the big picture? How is the customer's problem related to other real or potential problems?
>
> - What is going to happen next to this customer?
>
> - What might this customer not know?
>
> - Where have others gotten into trouble concerning this issue?
>
> - What is the impact of *not* solving the problem?

6. Follow up

Check back with the customer to make sure you've achieved satisfaction. If the answer is yes, you've closed on a positive note. If no, you now have a second chance to make things right with the customer.

Key Elements of a Service Recovery Plan

- **Timeliness**. Problems are handled at the earliest opportunity, by the provider who discovers the problem when possible.

- **Commitment**. Genuine concern for the customer is demonstrated.

- **Empowerment**. Service providers have both the authority and the responsibility to solve problems.

- **Response strategy**. The customer receives both a "fair fix" and atonement for the inconvenience.

- **Prevention**. All team members are involved in preventing instances of dissatisfaction.

- **Evaluation**. Tangible evidence of results is presented, with attention given to plans for improvement.

Points to Remember

- The team member who uncovers a problem should take responsibility for finding a solution.

- Fact-finding uncovers the source of a problem, and often can point to larger issues to be addressed.

- Never go with the first solution that comes to mind—generate several solutions, then choose the one that will best deliver customer satisfaction.

- Uncovering additional, unspoken problems often saves the customer future inconvenience.

Exercise 20: Practice With Problem-Solving Skills

Question 1) What do we know so far about the student problem presented in this video segment?

Question 2) John seems to understand the problem well enough, so now it's time for him to ask fact-finding questions. What questions do you think you'd ask the customer in a case like this?

Exercise 21: Problem Solving and Service Recovery

Question 1) What are examples of ways that John follows the steps of service recovery?

1. Acknowledge the problem:_____

_____

2. Apologize: _____

_____

3. Problem solve: _____

_____

4. Communicate a solution and make amends: _____

_____

5. Implement a solution and follow up: _____

_____

Question 2) What is the impact of focusing on the student's problem rather than the institution's problem?

Question 3) How can we train ourselves to go beyond the institution's problem and focus on the customer's problem?

Question 4) Finally, the video made a point about not making promises for other staff members. Why do we do this? And what should we do instead?

SECTION 4: Meeting Challenges Caused By System Problems

In the last section you looked at service problems caused by institutional mistakes. Now it's time to look at system-driven problems. Every institution has systems, policies, and procedures that can cause big headaches for students—and staff. And system-driven problems can create the most difficult of all service recovery situations.

System-driven problems can be hard on your psyche, too. A customer is angry with you, yet you've done everything exactly by the book! The real problem, of course, is that sometimes the book needs to be rewritten, at least as far as this customer is concerned.

Let's look at a typical system-driven problem. Imagine you work in the business office, and a student comes to you requesting a refund for her fall term tuition. The student paid the tuition in full. Because classes haven't started yet, she is entitled to a full refund. However, there's a problem. Refund checks normally aren't sent to students until the sixth week of the term, after the last drop/add date. The student desperately needs her money back to help pay for a family emergency.

How would you handle this situation? You've empathized with the customer, apologized, problem solved and followed your department policy to the letter. The student, however, still is not satisfied.

On one level you are expected to follow the rules, but on another level you are expected to satisfy your customers. You can easily see the student's dilemma and, personally, you agree: the policy doesn't seem fair. Officially, however, there is nothing you can do. Or is there? System-driven problems are especially difficult, but not impossible, to recover from.

Take an Active Role in Eliminating System Problems

In earlier sections you discussed ways of working together as a team to provide quality service and improve your systems. When a system-driven problem arises, put those team-building skills to work. Asking questions and airing your concerns gets everyone involved. Group problem-solving sessions build relationships and expand your resources.

Try these ideas for eliminating system problems:

- Be proactive, rather than reactive.

- Keep track of customer problems that occur. Then, get together as a team and discuss each one. Is there a pattern to the problems? Are there ways to update your systems to prevent each problem from happening again?

- For those problems that can't be eliminated, look for ways to be prepared for the problems when they occur. Work together as a team to come up with consistent ways to handle difficult situations.

- Search for ways to prevent problems through customer education.

- Reward staff members who devise creative and effective problem-prevention strategies. Everyone on your team will feel better about making contributions when you know your efforts are noticed and appreciated!

In system-driven problems, quick fixes are often impossible. That doesn't mean there are no answers. You *can* deliver quality service even when a customer comes up against a "customer-unfriendly" procedure.

The role of staff in handling system-driven problems.
For staff, the primary responsibility is leaving no stone
unturned in efforts to help students and other customers
find solutions to their problems.

- Use empathy, understanding, knowledge, creativity,
  and persistence to help customers solve problems.

- Help to identify systems, policies, and procedures that
  cause problems for internal and external customers.

- Bring system-driven problems to the attention of
  administration so that they can be reviewed and
  changed if necessary.

**The role of administrators and faculty in handling
system-driven problems.** Administrators have a responsibility to work with staff to reduce the number of system-
driven problems.

- Teach staff how to deal with difficult system-driven
  problems.

- Remember that those closest to problems often have
  the best ideas for solutions. Empower staff to freely
  share and implement their ideas.

- Work to reduce or eliminate problems over which
  your office has responsibility.

- Work with administrators in other offices to identify
  and eliminate problems campuswide.

One important thing to remember with system-driven
problems is that finding a solution is not the only way to
make a customer happy. You can help people by providing quality service they feel good about, even if no acceptable solution is reached.

Things We Can Do to Prevent Problems

List your ideas for preventing problems for your customers, along with the first step you would take to put this plan into action.

Problem: _____

Idea: _____

First step: _____

Problem: _____

Idea: _____

First step: _____

Problem: _____

Idea: _____

First step: _____

Take that first step!

Points to Remember

- Work toward customer satisfaction even when you can't immediately change the system—it's still important.

- Demonstrate genuine caring and a desire to make things better in the future.

- Accept the authority and the responsibility to implement service recovery.

- Collaborate to resolve conflict.

- Every service provider has the responsibility to search for ways to prevent problems.

Exercise 22: Recovering From System Problems

Question 1) What's your gut reaction to this scenario? Can Jan recover from this?

Question 2) What would be a good first response for Jan to make in this situation? How could she apologize?

Question 3) What questions might you ask to start problem solving? Do you have any ideas now for possible solutions?

Question 4) What are some ways you might be able to make amends to this student?

Exercise 23: Preventing System Problems

Question 1) How do you feel about Jan's approach to the student?

Question 2) Could Jan have said or done anything more?

Question 3) Do you think the student left this encounter with negative or positive feelings?

Question 4) Is the institution's refund policy designed to serve the best interests of students or of the institution? In this encounter, who is the customer—the student or the institution?

Question 5) At our institution, what are examples of policies or procedures that work against the best interests of students?

Question 6) Jan's solution to the immediate problem is to turn the student over to the business office supervisor, yet she also offered to bring the matter up at a future meeting. What do you think of this approach to problem prevention? Whose responsibility is it to prevent problems?

Question 7) What are some ways each of us can work to prevent problems, so we won't continue to have unhappy customers?

Question 8) The video said that Jan missed an opportunity to try to keep the student in school. What are examples of ways in which you or your office promote student satisfaction and retention?

Optional Exercise: Test Your Service Recovery Skills—System Problems

Directions: Choose one or more of the following service situations as the subject for a role-play on recovering from system problems. Each role-play is designed for one service provider and one customer. The Role-Play Observation Checklist is provided for observers to note comments about the role-plays.

Situation 1: A faculty member calls the secretary at the physical plant. The faculty member is upset because she put in a work order 10 days ago to have a loose banister repaired in one of the classroom buildings, yet the work is still not done. She is concerned that someone will fall on the stairs, become injured, and possibly sue the institution. She can't understand why it takes so long to replace a couple of missing screws.

Situation 2: A parent who is the sole source of financial support for her daughter calls the institution to request a copy of her daughter's grades. The parent becomes furious when she is informed that the release of such information is a violation of federal law.

Situation 3: A student needs to drop one class and add another. This requires three signatures: the instructor of each class plus his advisor. His advisor and one of the instructors are available. The other instructor is out of town at a conference and won't be back until after the drop/add deadline. The student talks to a secretary from the department of the missing instructor.

Situation 4: A graduate student requests new materials for the library to assist her research in her field. The acquisitions librarian tells the student there are no funds available for her specialized request.

Situation 5: A prospective transfer engineering student calls the college of engineering to find out how his courses will apply to general education, major, and elective requirements. He is told by an assistant dean that engineering makes no binding commitments until after a student enrolls. The transfer student tells the dean he can't transfer without having that information.

Situation 6: A junior student has his registration canceled because he didn't pay his fall tuition on time. Two of the classes he needs to register for are now closed. His angry father complains to a business officer that this wouldn't happen if the tuition bills were sent home instead of to the student's campus address.

Situation 7: A student works 20 hours a week in the field house to help pay her bills. One pay period she doesn't get her check, which puts her in a real financial bind. After checking with payroll, she discovers that she didn't turn in her last time sheet because she was home sick the day it was due. The secretary in the payroll office tells the student they only cut student work checks once a week.

Role-Play Observation Checklist

Did _____, the service provider,
    (name)

	Yes	No
Show concern?	☐	☐
Take responsibility?	☐	☐
Make a positive first response?	☐	☐
Acknowledge the problem?	☐	☐
Apologize?	☐	☐
Problem solve?	☐	☐
Communicate solutions?	☐	☐
Make amends?	☐	☐
Plan for follow-up?	☐	☐

I particularly liked the way this service provider: _____

_____

_____

A possible area for improvement: _____

_____

_____

SECTION 5: Knowing When to Ask for Help

Being part of a team is great when all is going well. You enjoy the feeling of shared accomplishments, and often find that the strengths of the team seem to improve the strengths of each individual member.

Yet being part of a team also means being there for each other when there's a problem. For example, you notice a co-worker being confronted by an angry customer. If you're not much of a team player, you'll think to yourself, "Whew, I'm glad that's not *me* he's yelling at!" On the other hand, if you are a team player, you'll think to yourself, "Looks like Terry's in some trouble. I wonder if I can help?"

There are many advantages to bringing in another team member when you're confronted with a difficult customer service challenge. A team member can:

- Contribute a new set of skills and experience to the situation as a complement to your own skills.

- See the problem from a different viewpoint and be able to suggest a suitable solution.

- Provide a calming presence if the exchange is in danger of getting overheated.

Sometimes customers mistakenly believe that a problem with the system is really the fault of an individual service provider. When that happens, it can be nearly impossible to get over the roadblock the customer has erected. A team member can then come in, reassure the customer that his or her satisfaction is everyone's goal, and immediately depersonalize the conflict. Now the customer is more willing to listen and work to solve the problem.

When to Ask for Help From Your Team

The most experienced and successful service providers learn how to spot "team challenges" early in the customer contact. They know that getting help is sometimes the best way to serve the customer, and they do so without hesitation.

Be alert to the situations when you need the help of your team members. It's time to ask for help—

1. **When you, alone, can't satisfy the customer**

   Perhaps time constraints mean you need two or more people to get the job done on time. Maybe it's a signed approval you need. Perhaps you don't know how to perform a particular procedure, or the solution falls outside the normal parameters of your job. Ask for help.

2. **When the solution bends the rules**

   You and your team must establish which situations need prior authorization when it comes to bending the rules. Get authorization immediately to eliminate further inconvenience for your customer. Ask for help.

3. **When you've been unable to satisfy your customer**

   Sometimes your best efforts aren't good enough. If the customer is still dissatisfied, never say, "That's all I can do," and give up. Ask for help.

4. **When the customer's anger becomes personal**

   Remember that the process of customer service is as important as the outcome. A customer may have decided that he or she won't be satisfied by anything you do. Ask for help.

How to Ask a Team Member for Help

Asking for help—and getting the kind of help you need—can be easier when you're clear and concise about what needs to be done and when. Follow these steps:

Step	Example
1. State your purpose.	"I could really use your help with this student."
2. Describe problem and your solution.	"He says he paid his residence hall fees, but I can't find a record of it. While I check our records, could you call..."
3. Clearly state timeframe and ask for help.	"He's pretty upset and waiting in the lobby for an answer. Do you have time to help me right now?"
4. Offer your thanks after the customer is served.	"Thanks a lot for your your solution."

Empower Staff to Promote Service Excellence

"You'll have to talk to my supervisor" is a phrase that conjures up dread in the minds of most customers. All too often it means delays in getting a problem solved or repeating information and requests to another person. Being shuffled off to another person because your original service provider doesn't have the time, the interest, or the authority to help you can also suggest an evasion of responsibility.

There are two situations for which staff and managers need to work together to reduce the number of questions and problems referred to managers and supervisors. The first involves service situations staff need *training* to handle. The second involves situations in which staff only need *permission* to act. Consider the following examples:

When staff need training: An admissions office has a policy that all prospective students who call to check on the status of their application or the receipt of transcripts must be given that information only by professional staff. Three reasons for the policy are: 1) to provide the most accurate information to callers, 2) to best handle the follow-up questions that often accompany such calls, and 3) to protect staff from being put in the position of answering questions for which they might not feel comfortable or qualified.

The problem, of course, is that every such request by prospective students must be handled by *two* people instead of one. Service and responsiveness decline, and the workload is doubled for already busy people.

There is a solution, however, but it demands teamwork and training. With training and guidance, staff *could* help prospective students of certain kinds—for instance new students direct from high school whose files are simple and straightforward. Staff and managers might decide together that professional staff should handle the files of transfer students and returning adult learners.

When staff need permission: An alumni office requires that all requests for addresses of alumni be handled only by professional staff. In this and other common situations, staff members have the ability and information to respond, but they are prevented from doing so by policies or procedures. They aren't *empowered* to respond.

Every office or work group has service situations that could be handled by front-line staff with proper training, supervision, and permission to act. The challenge is to identify these situations and work together to develop a customer-centered service approach. As group, ask the following questions:

1. What requests, problems, or issues are routinely referred to managers and professional staff?

2. What requests, problems, or issues could be handled with guidance and supervision by front-line staff?

3. What requests, problems, or issues should always be referred to managers and professional staff?

Empowerment is an important part of your quality service plan because it gives each member of your team the authority to take responsibility and lead customers to acceptable solutions. When you work as a team, you need to make sure each person has the knowledge and resources they need to help customers. When staff are empowered to help customers and to perform service recovery, your service will be responsive and accountable. Training and teamwork lead to better service and better staff morale.

Points to Remember

- Team members can be powerful allies when it comes to satisfying unhappy customers.

- Empower front-line staff to serve customer needs quickly and responsibly.

- Training and teamwork lead to better service and better staff morale.

- In your office or work group, develop guidelines for when to refer requests, problems, and issues.

Exercise 24: Knowing When to Ask for Help

Question1) When and how do *you* call on your team for help?

Question 2) What guidelines do you have in your office for referring a customer to a supervisor? What guidelines would you *like* to have?

Question 3) Helping a team member when asked is really another way of providing internal customer service. How does improving your internal customer service improve external customer satisfaction?

Question 4) *Example 1*: An admissions office requires that all prospective students who call to check on the status of their application or the receipt of transcripts must be given that information by professional staff. *Example 2*: An alumni office requires that all requests for addresses of alumni be handled only by professional staff.

Question 5) What are some reasons offices have policies like these?

Question 6) Think of your own work area. What are examples of situations staff normally refer to supervisors that could be handled by staff?

SECTION 6: Problem Solving Through Customer Education

E arlier in the program you talked about problem solving within your work group or office. Problem solving can also be used to prevent problems by educating your customers about systems they deal with every day.

The Expert Is in

You may not think of yourself as an expert, but you are. No one else knows as much about your job as you do. The resources and techniques you use to solve problems can be taught to your customers. Teaching customers about the systems and procedures at your institution doesn't just help solve immediate problems. It empowers customers and encourages them to try solving problems on their own in the future.

Class Is in Session

One of the main goals of a college or university is to make students independent learners—learners who take responsibility for their own education. Similarly, one of the main goals in a service culture is to educate students and parents to be more independent customers—more knowledgeable, responsible, and self-sufficient.

In the video scene of the library assistant and the student trying to locate a missing book, the library assistant helped the student. More importantly, she taught the student how the library works so that next time the student will be better able to solve her own problems.

In every service contact *you* are a teacher. You have opportunities to teach students and other customers how to use your services more efficiently in ways that help you *and* your customers. For instance, imagine you work at the front desk in an office in which there are chronically long lines for students at certain times of the day. When students finally get to the front of the line, you could help them see that there are steps they can take to get better service:

- "I'm sorry you had to wait in line so long. The next time, if you come in before 10:00 or after 3:30, you won't have to stand in line as long."

- "Did you know that you can mail in this form instead of dropping it off in person?"

The Big Picture

It's important to let your customers know that you are always there to help them if they need it. Teaching them to help themselves isn't a ploy to get rid of them, and it doesn't mean you don't have time for them. Help them understand that you are giving them a tool, not a brush-off. You can do this by putting the information you give them into the big picture.

An orientation course for new students can provide a powerful opportunity to help all new students become more self-sufficient and more intelligent consumers of educational programs and services.

By taking responsibility for educating your customers, you promote quality service and prevent recurring problems.

Points to Remember

- Help your customers learn how to solve their own problems.

- Shared problem solving helps both internal and external customers.

- Teach your customers to be more intelligent consumers of educational programs and services.

- Recognize that it might require more effort *up front* to educate customers so that they can become more self-sufficient.

Exercise 25: Preventing Problems Through Education

Question 1) What would you say to a person who says, "Telling your customers how to solve their own problems is really just shoving your job off on them?"

Question 2) What are some ways we teach students to be better customers?

Question 3) What are some ways we teach parents to be better customers?

Question 4) What are some ways you could teach your customers to use your office or services better? Write your ideas below.

I could teach my *internal* customers how to: _____

_____

_____

_____

I could teach my *external* customers how to: _____

_____

_____

_____

SECTION 7: Action Planning!

Throughout Advanced Connections, you've explored a variety of skills and approaches that go into building a service culture on campus. You've practiced advanced service skills and explored ways to provide strong service recovery. You've learned that building a service culture requires a customer-centered focus. It also requires energy, creativity, and action from all staff, faculty, and administrators.

Now it's time to apply these skills and approaches to your own work and, through teamwork, to the work of your office or department.

Action Planning for Real Campus Situations

To illustrate the principles and methods for building a service culture presented in Advanced Connections, consider this example of a typical service challenge.

Service challenge: The setting is a registrar's office on a busy pre-registration day. Although students receive a pre-assigned registration time, they frequently wait in line up to an hour to start the registration process. When they reach the head of the line to pick up registration packets, they are informed about any "holds" on their registrations due to unpaid financial obligations such as past due tuition, parking and library fines, etc.

If students have holds, they must go to each office responsible for the hold and pay any monies due. They pick up clearances for the holds and return to the registrar's office where they stand at the back of the line and start the registration process all over again. This problem, which infuriates students and makes the lives of front-line staff miserable, affects large numbers of students and occurs every pre-registration day every term.

Service challenges like the run-around described above are all too common at colleges and universities. To meet the challenge and end the run-around, many different individuals and offices on campus need to work together to develop and implement a better service strategy. The grid on page 159 illustrates in very simplified form the possible roles that could be played by various offices and individuals. The key here is that everyone—from the president to front-line staff—has a part to play in building a service culture.

Action Group	Current Situation	New Procedures	New Policies	New Systems
Front-line staff	Use individual service skills to provide the best service possible under current conditions.	Suggest and help to implement new procedures such as informing students of registration holds in advance.	Suggest and help to implement new policies such as waiving registration holds for amounts under $25.	Suggest and help to implement new systems such as phone registration or unified billing.
Administrators and department heads	Model best service behaviors. Mentor and support staff to provide best possible service.	Devise and implement new procedures in own offices.	Work with other administrators to devise and implement new policies.	Work with other administrators to devise and implement new systems.
Cabinet-level officers	Make a public commitment to campuswide service excellence. Support training to promote service excellence.	Encourage and empower staff and administrators to find solutions for current problems.	Facilitate communication and solutions across divisions. Approve new policies.	Facilitate communication and solutions across divisions. Approve and fund new registration systems.

Evaluation

The idea of building a service culture may be a new concept to your area. Having a solid evaluation system will help people see the improvement quality service makes. Of course, team members will feel the improvement, your office or department will run more smoothly, and your team members will have better relations with internal and external customers, but quantitative analysis can be a powerful reinforcing tool.

Beyond the campuswide benchmark measures of student recruitment and student retention, look for measures of service excellence that make sense for you and your work area. Refer to Session Two, Section 7: Checking for Customer Satisfaction for some possibilities.

Working Together for a Smarter Tomorrow

You've seen how your efforts to build a quality service culture can help improve your service and make your job easier and more enjoyable. Building a service culture helps your office work together more effectively to reach solutions.

Most important, by working together you will play a crucial role in helping students learn and grow in an environment that is convenient, supportive, and free of obstacles to success.

Role of front-line staff in building a service culture

- Provide quality service to internal and external customers in every contact.
- Teach customers to be more intelligent consumers of your programs and services.
- Partner with administrators in identifying and solving problems.
- Continuously learn about your job, your office, and the institution.

Role of managers and department heads in building a service culture

- Model the best service attitude and behavior.

- Become a coach and mentor for staff and student employees on quality service issues and performance.

- Make your office user-friendly for your internal and external customers.

- Provide a thorough orientation for new staff and ongoing training and development for experienced staff and student employees.

- Empower staff. Include staff in decision making.

- Identify and solve service problems within your own office.

- Work with managers and department heads in other offices to identify and solve service problems.

- Improve communication with other offices.

Role of faculty in building a service culture

- Create a learning environment in the classroom that focuses on individual student needs.

- Provide high quality academic services such as academic advising.

- Identify and help to solve system problems that negatively affect students, staff, and faculty.

- Be timely and accurate in grade reports, book orders, and other academic procedures.

- Be an advocate for student-centered course scheduling—offering courses that students need at the times they are free to take them.

- Know the campus personnel and academic resources to which you can refer students.

- Respond in a positive way to student evaluations.

- Be available for students by establishing—and honoring—office hours that are student-centered.

Role of upper-level administrators in building a service culture

- Make a public commitment to service goals and to the importance of building a service culture.

- Charge managers and department heads with the responsibility of developing service goals and standards.

- Support the service goals and strategies of administrative and academic units.

- Make training and development a top priority.

- Take leadership in coordinating cross-divisional functions and in solving service problems that cross reporting lines.

- Take leadership in measuring student, staff, manager, and faculty satisfaction.

- Hold all faculty, staff, and managers responsible for service performance.

Make Quality Service an Institutionwide Priority

Use the following agenda to build a service culture and make quality service an institutionwide commitment:

- Build quality service expectations into job descriptions and performance evaluations.

- Develop a meaningful and deliverable institutionwide quality service mission statement—a public commitment to quality service.

- Name a committee to oversee the planning and execution of an institutionwide quality service strategy.

- Help managers learn how to hire staff who will be good quality service agents by educating them about ways to interview for service skills.

- Encourage all members of the campus community to practice continuous learning and improvement.

- Develop a reward and recognition system for staff that is meaningful and that effectively promotes service excellence.

- Regularly invite the input of staff on institutional policies and procedures.

- Encourage administrative offices and faculty units to develop their own service statements and service strategies.

- Implement a quality service training program.

- Increase the training and supervision of part-time and student employees.

- Implement an extended orientation course to educate students about institutional policies and procedures.

- Regularly survey student attitudes about their interaction with offices and services.

Optional Exercise: Case Studies on Building a Service Culture

Directions: Use the following system problems as subjects for case studies using group problem-solving techniques. In each case, assume that the registrar's office, business office, and financial aid office report to a different vice president. As a group:

- Devise some possible solutions for the system problem.

- Determine possible approaches or paths for making the solution happen. (What would it take to solve the problem?)

- Determine which office or offices should take the lead in solving the problem.

Situation 1: At Oceanside State University, an entering transfer student can get informal transfer credit evaluations done before he enrolls. However, the registrar only records credit officially on the student's record after the student actually enrolls. Thus, as far as financial aid is concerned, the student is a freshman and his aid is packaged accordingly—with a $2,625 Stafford loan instead of the $3,500 or $5,000 for which he would qualify as a sophomore or junior.

Moreover, the system does not automatically correct itself after the student enrolls. He must visit the registrar to ensure that the credits are recorded, then go to the financial aid office to get the aid award changed, then wait for the state agency and bank to process the increased amount, then go to the business office to get the money. Meanwhile the student may be delinquent on his tuition or unable to pay his rent.

Situation 2: At Midwestern State University it is common for classes to be considered full and closed on the computerized registration system. Class sizes purposely are kept below capacity, and faculty routinely approve several more students to enroll in each closed class. However, these faculty permissions to enroll are rarely recorded officially until the drop/add period after the term starts. Meanwhile, when the financial aid office accesses official records in the registrar's office, some students are seen as less-than-full-time, and their aid is reduced accordingly or canceled.

The system is not self-correcting. A student caught in this bind must personally visit the registrar's office, the financial aid office, and the business office to correct the problem.

Intradepartmental Follow-up Exercise: A Blueprint for Service Excellence

Directions: After completing Advanced Connections, use the forms in this follow-up exercise to help you and your department focus your discussions and plan for success.

Institutions that provide consistently exceptional service are able to do so because they have a plan. They know exactly what they're trying to achieve and they know what steps to follow to reach the goal.

The five practical approaches to building a service culture are:

1. Discover customer requirements.

2. Develop service standards that promote excellence.

3. Design service strategies that work.

4. Deliver quality service through every contact.

5. Check for satisfaction.

Use the Action Planning Forms on the following pages to help you begin the planning process.

Form A, Identifying and Meeting Customer Requirements, helps you apply the steps of quality service to specific service situations.

Form B, Service Challenge Within Office or Work Group, helps you explore the roles to be played by staff and administrators in meeting a specific service challenge.

Form C, Service Challenge Involving More Than One Office or Work Group, helps you explore the roles to be played by staff and administrators in meeting more complex service challenges.

Form D, Planning for Telephone Excellence Within Office or Work Group, helps you explore techniques, standards, policies, and guidelines for telephone use within your office.

Form E, Steps to Take to Develop a Service Excellence Plan, helps you determine specific action steps and to fix responsibility and a timeline for them.

Action Planning Form A

Identifying and Meeting Customer Requirements

Customer Group/ Situation	Customer Requirements	Service Standards	Service Strategies	Evaluation Measures
1.				
2.				
3.				
4.				
5.				

Action Planning Form B

Service Challenge Within Office or Work Group

Description of service challenge: _____

Action Group	Current Situation	New Procedures	New Policies	New Systems
Front-line staff in your office				
Administrators in your office				

Action Planning Form C

Service Challenge Involving More Than One Office or Work Group

Description of service challenge: _____

Action Group	Current Situation	New Procedures	New Policies	New Systems
Front-line staff in your office				
Administrators in your office				
Faculty				
Administrators and department heads in other offices				
Cabinet-level officers				

169

Action Planning Form D

Planning for Telephone Excellence Within Office or Work Group

	Topics to Address	Sample Ideas, Techniques, Guidelines	Ideas, Strategies, Techniques for Your Office
Phone standards	Set office guidelines on phone use.	Answer phone before third ring. No holds more than 30 seconds. Return calls within one day. Etc.	
Office phone greeting	Decide standard office greeting.	"Thank your for calling the music department. This is Ellyn. How may I help you?"	
Voice mail guidelines, policies	Set office guidelines on voice mail use.	Standard content of personal greetings. Guidelines for frequency of changing greeting. Etc.	
Phone transfer guidelines, policies	Set office guidelines on phone transfers.	Every caller given the name and number of the phone receiving the transfer, etc.	

Action Planning Form E

Steps to Take to Develop a Service Excellence Plan

Directions: Use this form to help you and your department determine specific action steps to implement ideas you learned throughout Advanced Connections.

To develop service excellence with the following groups:

☐ Students ☐ Co-workers

☐ Parents ☐ Other departments

☐ Alumni ☐ _____

☐ Community ☐ _____

1. Step: _____

   Person responsible: _____

   Due date: _____

2. Step: _____

   Person responsible: _____

   Due date: _____

3. Step: _____

   Person responsible: _____

   Due date: _____

4. Step: _____

   Person responsible: _____

   Due date: _____

5. Step: _____

   Person responsible: _____

   Due date: _____

My Commitment to Self-Development

As a result of what I've learned today, I am making a commitment to work toward improvement in these areas:

1. _____

2. _____

3. _____

4. _____

5. _____

6. _____

7. _____

I will ask _____ to help me check my
　　　　　　　(Co-worker's name)

progress on _____.
　　　　　　　　　(Date)